HOME OFFICE RESEARCH STUDY NO. 92

The effectiveness of the Forensic Science Service

by Malcolm Ramsay

A HOME OFFICE RESEARCH AND PLANNING UNIT REPORT

LONDON: HER MAJESTY'S STATIONERY OFFICE

ISBN 0 11 340842 0

HOME OFFICE RESEARCH STUDIES

'Home Office Research Studies' comprise reports on research undertaken in the Home Office to assist in the exercise of its administrative functions, and for the information of the judicature, the services for which the Home Secretary has responsibility (direct or indirect) and the general public.

On the last pages of this report are listed titles already published in this series, in the preceding series *Studies in the Causes of Delinquency and the Treatment of Offenders,* and in the series of *Research and Planning Unit Papers.*

Her Majesty's Stationery Office

Standing order service

Placing a standing order with HMSO BOOKS enables a customer to receive other titles in this series automatically as published.

This saves time, trouble and expense of placing individual orders and avoids the problem of knowing when to do so.

For details please write to HMSO BOOKS (PC13A/1), Publications Centre, PO Box 276, London, SW8 5DT and quoting reference X25.08.07.

The standing order service also enables customers to receive automatically as published all material of their choice which additionally saves extensive catalogue research. The scope and selectivity of the service has been extended by new techniques, and there are more than 3,500 classifications to choose from. A special leaflet describing the service in detail may be obtained on request.

Foreword

This is the first substantial published study of the working and effectiveness of the Forensic Science Service. Both scientists and police officers responsible for a large number of cases were interviewed in the preparation of the report and a comprehensive picture was built up of the work of forensic laboratories. Forensic analysis assisted the police in over two out of three cases referred to the laboratories. Those police forces making relatively high use of the Forensic Science Service found the service to be helpful at least as frequently as did those which made fewer referrals. The report suggests that scope exists for improving relationships between the Forensic Science Service and the police, and makes some suggestions as to how such improvements could be achieved.

MARY TUCK
Head of the Research and Planning Unit

December 1986

Acknowledgements

I am most grateful to staff of the Forensic Science Service at the Birmingham and Huntingdon laboratories who participated in this research; also to the many police officers in Bedfordshire, Derbyshire, Essex and West Midlands who were involved, whether as interviewees or in the project's planning and organisation. So many scientists and police officers played a part in the project in one way or another that it would be wrong to single out any individuals. Particular thanks are however due to the two researchers who assisted me with fieldwork, Michael Morrogh and Ruth Trenbirth. Both of them contributed significantly to the project over and above the collection of data and interviewing. I would also like to thank staff at the Huntingdon laboratory for their account of the case of 'the Fox', which has been included in Appendix C.

MALCOLM RAMSAY

Contents

1 Introduction

This report presents the results of a study examining the effectiveness of the Home Office Forensic Science Service in England and Wales. A brief introduction to the Forensic Science Service (FSS) is provided in this chapter, which also discusses other relevant studies and sets out the aims and methods of the research. Chapter 2 describes the cases that were studied, while chapter 3 examines the extent to which the work done by the FSS proved helpful to the police. Chapter 4 looks at police attitudes towards the FSS, and at the pattern of working relationships between police officers and scientists. A summary and conclusions are presented in the last chapter.

What does the Forensic Science Service do?

The FSS, although not a secret organisation, has tended to adopt a low profile towards the outside world. Even some police officers—including those who have actually made use of it—feel unsure as to what it can or cannot do. Little has ever been published about its work, apart from technical material or accounts of some of its more unusual cases. The FSS itself does not produce an annual report to which interested members of the public might turn for general information.

The FSS exists to provide impartial information about cases submitted to it involving physical evidence from scenes of crime, such as broken glass or blood-stained clothes. Staff of the FSS are not medically qualified although some, as biologists or chemists trained to degree level or beyond, carry out sophisticated analyses of human remains. (The Forensic Pathology Service, a small, separately organised group of doctors, is called upon by the courts to provide medical explanations of causes of death.) Forensic scientists do not normally even deal with fingerprints, generally the most clear-cut form of physical evidence to be looked for at scenes of crime. These are handled by the fingerprint officers—usually civilians—of individual police forces.

The work of forensic scientists is wide-ranging: grouping blood stains or semen from the victim of an assault or a rape; examining the remains of a burnt-out school, to see whether the fire was caused by arson; ascertaining whether a footprint found at the scene of a crime corresponds with a suspect's shoe, or whether fragments of glass adhering to someone's clothes match those from a broken window. A basic principle of forensic science, formulated by one of the founding fathers of the discipline—Locard—is that every contact leaves a trace. If one person strikes another, puts a boot through a window, brushes against the clothing of another person, pulls their hair, or whatever else, then splashes of blood, or tiny fragments of glass, or minute pieces of fibre or the odd few hairs will tend to attach themselves to whoever is responsible (or to their clothing or implements).

After a scientist has been called to the scene of a crime and has subsequently examined the evidence—or, much more usually, after he has simply analysed key exhibits selected by the police—he writes a report. This is sent to the police, who are responsible for passing it to the prosecution, if appropriate. It is the responsibility of the prosecution—if it is anticipated that the evidence will be required at the trial—to serve it on the defence. Either the written report alone may be presented in court, or the scientist may also appear in person when he is likely to be subject to cross-examination.

The FSS is independent of the police: it is part of the Home Office, and its staff are civil servants. It has a fairly good—though not always close—working relationship with the police. Its staff, numbering over 450 scientists, is now grouped in six operational laboratories throughout England and Wales, and a separate research establishment. (In addition, the Metropolitan Police has its own laboratory, which is also used by the City of London Police, but is not part of the FSS.)

Scientific accuracy or quality control, even though it falls outside the scope of this report, is an issue which demands at least some consideration in this introductory chapter. The work of the FSS has undoubtedly become increasingly sophisticated since its early days in the nineteen thirties and forties. In a working environment increasingly dominated by computerised equipment which allows the results of tests to be automatically recorded in a permanent form, "quality assurance", as it is known in the FSS, has become more attainable. Individual scientists no longer work so much on their own as happened formerly; co-operation and double-checking is now routine.

If the FSS over the last few years has vigorously pursued scientific accuracy and efficiency, less attention has been paid to the role and effectiveness of the FSS within the criminal justice system. Of course, these wider considerations have not been ignored by the FSS, which has itself carried out some enquiries. Up till now, however, no empirical research has been undertaken in any depth on the extent to which the work of the FSS assists the police and the courts in solving crimes and in bringing offenders to justice.

Vital statistics of the Forensic Science Service

The overall FSS caseload for 1984 is shown in table 1. Almost half consists of cases of drunken-driving ("driving under influence"), involving semi-automated analysis of blood-alcohol levels. Drug offences comprise a further fifth of cases, a good many of which are comparatively straightforward. The

2

Table 1
Caseload of the Forensic Science Service, 1984

Category	Number of cases	%	
Homicide	422	1	
Woundings, other woundings	1,147	2	
Sexual cases	1,508	2	
Burglary	3,030	5	18%
Robbery	343	1	
Theft	1,673	3	
Arson	1,370	2	
Criminal damage	1,332	2	
Coinage	17	<1	
Explosives	150	<1	
Safes	10	<1	
Unclassified	816	1	
Sudden death, alcohol/toxicological	1,346	2	14%
Firearms	1,210	2	
Documents	2,236	4	
Tachographs	244	<1	
Traffic accidents	2,459	4	
Driving under influence (alcohol)	29,101	48	68%
Drugs	12,441	20	
Total	60,855	100	

Note
The first eight categories or groupings follow, approximately, definitions used by *Criminal Statistics*.

remaining 17 categories—accounting for less than a third of all cases—are classified partly in terms of offences or incidents, and partly in terms of the different sorts of objects involved.

Cases other than drugs or driving under influence, although only accounting for a comparatively small proportion of the total caseload, are important in terms of the resources they absorb and their intrinsic seriousness. Table 2 shows—for the eight categories which can be matched, at least approximately, with corresponding terms in *Criminal Statistics*—the proportion of crimes recorded by the police which was referred to the FSS in 1980 and 1984. Between those years the percentage of cases referred fell for all categories except homicide; even the absolute number dropped for all types except homicide and robbery. Overall, the number of these types of cases dealt with by the FSS sank from 13,937 to 10,825.

A number of factors contributed to this reduction. The increased emphasis on quality control has meant that some sorts of cases have been looked at in greater detail. Above all, following a Rayner review completed in 1981,

Table 2

Eight key categories of FSS caseload figures and crime statistics, 1980 and 1984, England and Wales except London

Category	1980			1984		
	Total recorded crimes	*No. of cases to FSS*	*% of cases to FSS*	*Total recorded crimes*	*No. of cases to FSS*	*% of cases to FSS*
Homicide	415	327	79	457	422	92
Woundings, other woundings	79,654	1,478	2	93,148	1,147	1
Sexual cases	18,271	1,873	10	17,150	1,508	9
Burglary	494,253	4,720	1	727,612	3,030	<1
Robbery	7,363	312	4	11,245	343	3
Theft (and handling)	1,138,980	1,888	<1	1,429,209	1,673	<1
Arson	10,446	1,641	16	15,051	1,370	9
Damage	135,701	1,698	1	223,949	1,332	1
Total	1,885,083	13,937	1	2,517,821	10,825	<1

Notes
1. In 1980, police forces for Essex, Hertfordshire, Kent, Surrey and Sussex still used the Metropolitan Police laboratory rather than the FSS establishments, but data for those forces have nonetheless been incorporated in this table.
2. Figures for recorded crimes of damage are for offences involving a loss of over £20.

the FSS has explicitly discouraged the police from submitting cases with little potential pay-off, especially those where a suspect is likely to plead guilty anyway.

Contrasts between police forces

The extent to which individual police forces make use of the FSS varies substantially. This remains true even when differences between police forces are taken into account. Here was an additional conundrum on which the research was designed to shed some light. Do forces making higher—or lower—than average use of the FSS gain or lose differentially in their use of the FSS? The extent of the variation can be gauged from table 3. This 'league table' sets out figures for forces using two out of the six FSS laboratories (Huntingdon and Birmingham, those where the research was carried out), and is restricted to the eight key categories where the FSS classifications approximately match those of *Criminal Statistics* (homicides, woundings, sexual cases, burglary, robbery, theft, arson and criminal damage). The table shows that, in 1984, Bedfordshire submitted over three times as many cases per police officer to its local laboratory as some of the other

4

Table 3
Use of the Birmingham and Huntingdon laboratories by customer police forces, for the eight key crime categories, in 1984, with figures for the relevant crimes per force/officer.

	Officers per force	Refer-rals to lab	Refer-rals to lab per officer	Crimes per force	Refer-rals per 1,000 crimes	Crimes per officer
*Bedford (H)	994	214	.22	32,041	6.7	32.2
Northants (H)	1,010	156	.15	30,625	5.1	30.3
*W Midlands (B)	6,524	908	.14	220,854	4.1	33.9
Cambs (H)	1,136	148	.13	28,991	5.1	25.5
W Mercia (B)	1,897	239	.13	44,633	5.4	23.5
Suffolk (H)	1,127	131	.11	23,119	5.7	20.5
Herts (H)	1,580	179	.11	35,859	5.0	22.7
*Essex (H)	2,649	299	.11	60,250	5.0	22.7
Staffs (B)	2,103	214	.10	47,302	4.5	22.5
Warwicks (B)	916	91	.10	20,807	4.4	22.7
Lincs (H)	1,152	97	.08	24,916	3.9	21.6
*Derby (B)	1,761	139	.08	43,717	3.2	24.8
Norfolk (H)	1,260	91	.07	32,156	2.8	25.5
Leics (H)	1,703	98	.06	41,163	2.4	24.2
Notts (H)	2,220	125	.06	81,480	1.5	36.7

Notes
1. The forces have been ranked according to their rate of referral of cases to the FSS, per officer (column 3, numbering from left).
2. Forces using Birmingham are followed by a B, those using Huntingdon by an H.
3. The four forces involved in the research have been marked with asterisks.
4. The eight key categories are homicide, woundings, sexual cases, burglary, robbery, theft, arson and criminal damage.

forces. This kind of variation—which is to be found right across the country—cannot simply be explained away in terms of the differing workloads of the various forces, as signified by the number of crimes per officer. The rank-order of forces would change to some extent if the number of referrals per 1,000 crimes was adopted as the relevant indicator. However, this indicator is distorted by variations in the reporting and recording of offences, so the research, for ranking purposes, relies instead on the number of referrals per officer—also a rough-and-ready substitute guide to the relative frequency of referrals per detective for the different forces—which in any event is the standard method followed by the FSS itself.

The investigation of crime by the police: research findings

This section provides, by way of context, a short review of previous research on forensic analysis, and more generally on the detection process. The main conclusion of researchers has been that detectives do not usually work as sleuths progressing from clue to clue in the manner of Sherlock Holmes; rather they process information supplied by members of the public. The detection of the vast mass of offences is a fairly open-and-shut matter. If the public can provide useful leads—a name, a good description, some indication of the likely culprit—the police may then be able to solve the crime or, rather, lay a firm basis for prosecution, especially if the suspect makes a confession when taken into custody and interviewed.

Research by David Steer (1980) exemplifies this view of detective work and also emphasises the limited contribution made by physical evidence, whether in the shape of forensic exhibits or fingerprints. He charted the strategies—both successful and unsuccessful—which were initially used by detectives to establish the identity of suspects. Apart from shoplifting cases and those cleared up when crimes were 'taken into consideration' at the request of the offender, Steer found that the successful strategy, roughly two out of three times in his main sample, and more than three out of four in a smaller sample of more serious offences,[1] was one which sprang directly or indirectly from information provided by members of the public who alerted the police or who provided key facts when interviewed by detectives.[2] Steer noted that a scene-of-crime examination was carried out quite frequently, especially in the case of the more serious group of offences, in order to show the methods used and to look for forensic clues (and fingerprints). Almost invariably—with a single exception in the serious cases, one which involved fingerprints—this was not a successful strategy in establishing the identity of a suspect.

Steer's conclusions are echoed by research in the United States. Peterson, Bender and Gilliland (1982) carried out a general review of research concerned with forensic science. They found that forensic evidence is only gathered in a small proportion of cases—and used in even fewer—despite the fact that, in theory, it can often be found at the scene of a crime. Peterson and his co-authors explain this disparity in various ways: laboratories are often very remote from the areas where investigators work; communications between laboratories and police are poor; and there is considerable pressure of work on American laboratories, especially from a massive volume of drugs cases. In stressing the routine nature of the investigation of crime—the building up of dossiers based on interviews with victims and witnesses—Peterson and his colleagues place special emphasis on the research by Greenwood and Petersilia (1975). According to this study, even the fairly small proportion of crime cleared up other than by information from the public tends to involve various non-technical procedures of a time-honoured nature. These include, in par-

---

[1] 'More serious' crimes were defined as those attracting life imprisonment (e.g. attempted murder, causing grievous bodily harm, rape, aggravated burglary, robbery, arson, affray, and criminal damage endangering life) and property offences involving sums of over £500.

[2] As categorised by Steer, this was where the suspect was caught red-handed (or at least was found in the vicinity of the crime), when his identity was known from the outset, when the victim provided a full description, when the suspect's motivation/opportunity was obvious, or as a result of house-to-house enquiries.

ticular, the investigation of receivers ('fences'), the cultivation of informants, and the extensive use of confessions made by offenders who, once caught for one offence, may well admit to many others.

Few researchers on either side of the Atlantic have specifically addressed themselves to the role of forensic science within the investigation of crime. The major studies of criminal investigation, including that by Greenwood and Petersilia, have mainly been concerned with fingerprints in evaluating the role of physical evidence. Rosenthal and Travnicek (1974) found that both forensic material and fingerprints were helpful to the prosecution: they were associated with a comparatively high proportion of immediate pleas of guilty, as opposed to guilty pleas made only as a result of plea bargaining.

The most detailed investigation to have been carried out in the United States into the effectiveness of physical evidence is that by Peterson, Mihajlovic and Gilliland (1983), which followed on from the 1982 study by Peterson and colleagues, already mentioned. The 1983 evaluation included fingerprint cases as well as forensic ones, and drew on records from laboratories, police, prosecution and court sources in four cities. It involved matched samples of robberies, aggravated assaults and burglaries (with and without physical evidence), together with further unmatched samples of other offences (notably rapes and homicides). Those cases of robbery, assault and burglary where physical evidence was available had significantly higher rates of clearances and convictions. For the homicides and the rapes—where comparisons could not be made between cases with and without physical evidence—different sorts of scientific findings had different kinds of impact. Cases where the laboratory report linked the suspect to the victim had a positive outcome more frequently than did cases with other scientific conclusions, although the difference only reached statistical significance in two out of the four jurisdictions. Such variations between different localities emerge as a highly important factor in this study. So does the interaction of physical evidence with other forms of evidence upon the final disposition of the cases.

Peterson and his colleagues do not claim—even for the United States—to have pinpointed precisely where and how forensic evidence makes a differ-ence. They do however confirm the argument of Steer and other researchers that forensic evidence does not usually solve cases by itself, but rather that it can strengthen investigations and prosecutions where other evidence is also available.

One gap in criminological literature—whether British or American—is the lack of attention paid to the investigation of especially serious crimes. On an anecdotal basis, forensic science is often justified by pointing to its success in helping to solve some especially sensational offence. Studies such as that by Peterson and his colleagues, concerned as they are with broad samples, are not especially helpful on this point. However, to the English reader, the extremely violent nature of quite a few of the case-histories recounted by

Peterson and his co-authors suggests that, if they had been committed in this country, they would have ranked alongside the very worst of our own offences. In that sense, the Peterson research implies that forensic science can make a useful contribution to bringing to justice those offenders whose misdeeds are a matter of notoriety.

Design of the present study

This research involved detailed examination of a sample of some 600 cases where the police sought the help of the FSS in 1984. (A handful of cases from early 1985 was also included.) Instead of providing thin coverage of the whole range of cases handled by the FSS, attention was concentrated on the broad group of crimes against people or property usually tackled by the two main departments of FSS laboratories: homicides, woundings, sexual cases, burglaries, robberies, thefts, arson and damage, together with small groups of cases involving coinage, explosives, safes and miscellaneous offences. These cases are very much those which preoccupy the FSS (and the CID in police forces). At a rough estimate, the twelve categories studied account for some two-thirds of the total effort of the FSS, as measured in scientist manhours. The sample excluded cases of drugs and 'driving under influence'—the two highest-volume and relatively routine components of the FSS caseload—together with five other groups, several of them dealt with by distinct specialist departments: firearms, documents, tachographs, traffic accidents and sudden deaths.

The sample was drawn from two out of the six FSS laboratories in England and Wales: Birmingham and Huntingdon. At each laboratory, sequences of about 150 consecutive cases were drawn from a pair of the half-dozen or so police forces which used their services. Derbyshire and West Midlands were chosen for Birmingham, and Bedfordshire and Essex for Huntingdon. These four forces represented a range of sizes, workloads, and rates of referral to the FSS.

For each case in the sample, basic facts—the type of crime that was involved, the nature of the exhibits, the kind of conclusions reached—were extracted from the relevant file at the laboratory, and written down on a data collection form by a member of the research team. Special attention was paid to the HOLAB (the form filled in by the police when submitting the exhibits), and to the report compiled by the scientist responsible for the case. If available, the scientist was asked to complete a questionnaire about the case and his dealings with the police and the courts. Finally, in a subsample of 395 cases, stratified by police divisions and chosen by skipping every third case, the police officer in charge of the investigation was selected for interview. (One small deviation was that, in Derbyshire, where there was a large group of interrelated cases of theft of electricity, an arbitrary quota was used to limit the numbers of these cases.) The police officers were asked further details about their cases and about the part played by the work of the FSS, together with some more general, open-ended questions. (The data collection form and the scientist and police questionnaires are set out in full in Appendix E.)

The total number of cases in the sample for which a data collection form was completed was 593; scientists answered their questionnaire in 547 cases; and 330 police officers out of the subsample were successfully interviewed. Further information about the samples is presented in Appendix A.

One last point should be made about the sampling process. At Huntingdon, work on exhibits associated with 'the Fox'—a lone burglar turned sex offender whose extensively publicised depredations caused considerable alarm—actually fell, in part, within the Bedfordshire case sample. A series of related incidents was involved, some in different parts of the country, and altogether over 800 exhibits were received of which more than 600 were examined (80 would normally be very rare for a single case). Given the highly unusual nature of this case, it was obvious that it would have fitted awkwardly into the general sample, and that it was better to look at it separately. An account of 'the Fox' forms part of Appendix C; it makes an interesting case-study of the kind of contribution which the FSS can make to the investigation of exceptionally serious crime.

2 The cases submitted by the police to the laboratories

This chapter describes the cases submitted to the two laboratories, the objectives of the police in enlisting the assistance of the FSS, and the allocation of the work within the laboratories. The data collection forms (covering all 593 cases) and the police questionnaires (covering 330 cases) are the main sources of information; the much shorter scientist questionnaires (547 cases) are also drawn upon.

Profile of cases referred to FSS

Table 1 provides a breakdown of the sample by crime type. Roughly 30 per cent of the 593 cases involved 'violence against the person' (homicide and woundings) and sexual offences. Burglary, robbery and theft comprised approximately 40 per cent of the total. The remainder accounted for less than 30 per cent, the largest group being damage—nearly two-thirds of which involved arson. The distribution of the types of case in the sample corresponded very closely with the actual distribution of the FSS's workload of cases among the sampled categories (see Appendix A, table 1).

Table 1
Breakdown of selected offences submitted by four police forces to the laboratories in 1984, by offence type.

Criminal Statistics categories	No.	%
Violence against the person	98	17
Sexual offences	84	14
Burglary	132	22
Robbery	16	3
Theft (and handling)	96	16
Damage (all forms including arson)	154	26
Fraud/forgery	3	1
Other	10	2
Total	593	100

Cases referred to the FSS tend to be fairly serious. In 192 of the 593 cases—almost a third—one or more people suffered physical injury: this is a far higher proportion than applies to crimes in general. Victims died in 30 cases, and underwent a sexual assault in a further 82; there were also 32 cases in which a victim went to hospital at least overnight, and another 48 where they suffered some lesser form of injury. There can be little doubt that, in many of the remaining 138 cases in which individual victims were identified, these people suffered some of the less tangible after-effects of victimisation, which cannot be calibrated quite so readily.

Two-thirds of the 330 cases covered by police questionnaires involved some measure of financial loss, either to an individual or to an institution. (Nearly all the corporate victims suffered in this way; so too did roughly half the personal victims). The costs involved in 8 per cent of cases were in excess of £10,000. Nearly three quarters of this small group of expensive incidents took the form of arson, the enormously costly nature of which is often overlooked since its impact is generally cushioned by insurance. Otherwise, in 22 per cent of cases the loss caused either through damage or theft was estimated to have been upwards of £500; in 19 per cent it was at least £100; and in 18 per cent the loss was either less than £100 or else was uncertain. By comparison with national figures in *Criminal Statistics,* the cases in the FSS sample involved higher losses. For instance, in 1984, according to *Criminal Statistics,* the value of the stolen property exceeded £500 in less than a quarter of all household burglaries. By contrast, in the sample of cases covered by the police questionnaire, over half the residential burglaries involved losses over £500.

The aims and expectations of the police

Cases where a suspect had been identified at the time of referral accounted for a high proportion of the total: 79 per cent of the 330 in the police sample. The FSS was not asked to reveal 'who dunnit', but to corroborate suspicions already well formed.

How then were suspects identified? In 25 per cent of cases with suspects they had been singled out either by name or by an equally revealing indicator such as a car number. In a further 28 per cent the police had been given a description of the suspect. In the remaining 47 per cent of cases with suspects the police were without eyewitness testimony. Of course, a name put forward by a victim or witness did not necessarily mean that the investigating officer's task was at an end: the assembling of adequate evidence to support a prosecution was just as important as establishing an initial identification.

It was FSS policy not to examine cases where a suspect might be expected to plead guilty, perhaps on the basis of having made a confession. Apart from a few exceptional cases—mostly homicides—where additional information was wanted about some specific element of the case, the police turned to the FSS because their investigations needed to be deepened if they were to be sure of gaining a conviction. There were, for instance, hardly any cases where the police had identified a suspect on the basis of fingerprint marks, perhaps the most obviously damning form of evidence where it exists—providing the suspect lacks legitimate access.

Most officers who were interviewed made it clear that they had attached considerable importance to the prospect of FSS assistance: 270 out of the 330 said that they had hoped that crucial, important or useful evidence would come to light from the work of the FSS. That only left 60 officers who indicated that they had turned to the FSS either as a matter of routine, or just in case something came up. The cases where officers were most likely to have had high hopes of the FSS when they contacted it tended to be those where a suspect had already been identified, as table 2 shows.

Table 2
Police officers' expectations of the FSS, and whether or not a suspect had been identified.

	Police hoped for crucial or important evidence	Police hoped for useful evidence	Police not very hopeful	Total (n = 330)
	%	%	%	%
Suspect identified (n = 262)	60	27	13	100
No suspect identified (n = 68)	32	29	38	100

Note:
Table 2 draws on questions 9 and 22 of the police questionnaire.

Although the officers generally had high hopes of the FSS, their decision to seek its help was sometimes taken as the last resort. In nearly half the cases, the police investigation was at a halt while the FSS was at work. And even when police enquiries were still continuing, they rarely seemed to be breaking fresh ground. In other words, the police were apt to turn to the FSS not just because they lacked sufficient alternative sources of information, but because they had exhausted all, or nearly all, of the other avenues open to them.

What precisely were the aims of the police? This question was explored both by asking the officers what their objective had been, and by analysing the referral form (the HOLAB, the document which accompanies the exhibits from the police to the FSS). While there were some differences between the respective sets of evaluations by researchers and police, the objective stated

13

most frequently by the police, and also identified most often by the researchers, was the strengthening or validation of a case against a suspect. In diminishing order of importance, the other four objectives were: to see if or how a crime had been committed; to analyse items for future reference; to help identify an unknown offender; and "other". Of these four, the last three were comparatively rare.

In over half the full sample (313 cases, or 53 per cent of all 593), the key function asked of the FSS was to link or match different substances or items to a common origin or source. A further 39 per cent (231) involved the identification of various items or substances: for instance, analysis of debris from a fire to determine whether an accelerant such as petrol was used, or the examination of swabs taken from the victim of some form of sexual assault to check, for instance, for the presence of any semen. Together, these two functions accounted for over nine-tenths of the total sample. Open-ended trawling of exhibits to look for any possible clues only accounted for 7 per cent (43 cases). Virtually every time that the FSS was asked to look for a link between items, a suspect had—almost by definition—been identified; this was also true of just over half the cases where the laboratories were simply requested to determine the nature of an item or substance.

In the comparatively small proportion of cases—around a fifth—where a suspect had not been identified before the referral of exhibits, the FSS was being used to see if further police investigation was needed, or to suggest or to narrow down possible lines of enquiry. Over a third of these cases involved suspected arson: the FSS was asked to determine whether the fire had been started deliberately, and the methods used. The special expertise of the FSS was apparent in some of these cases, including one involving a fire in a school which caused damage of the order of £250,000, and which was attributed by the fire brigade to an electrical fault. When the FSS subsequently found clear traces of arson, police were then able to use their local knowledge to conduct a successful investigation. Apart from arson, the only other distinct' group of offences lacking a suspect at referral was composed of rapes and other forms of sexual assault. The seriousness of these cases, coupled with the perishability of semen and other human matter, may have persuaded the investigating officer to send items to the FSS even if he had not immediately identified a suspect.

The response of the laboratories

Cases received by the laboratories were each assigned to one of the specialist departments. Sometimes a second department would also become involved. The largest group of cases—58 per cent—was handled by the chemistry department. These tended to comprise offences against property—in particular, arson, burglary, theft and damage. The biology department took responsibility for 40 per cent of cases. These were predominantly crimes of violence—sexual offences, woundings and homicide.

Not surprisingly, the nature of the items in cases handled by the biology and chemistry departments differed significantly. Cases where the chemistry department took the lead tended to involve footwear, glass, tracks or impressions, parts of motor vehicles, and tools or toolmarks. Biology department cases comprised, in particular, sexual or other biological matter such as saliva or faeces, clothing or fibres, blood, hair and weapons other than firearms.

A small minority of cases (2 per cent) was tackled in the first instance by other departments (toxicology/drugs and, in one case, firearms), although one or other of the two main departments also participated. In almost one in five of the 238 cases where the biology department took the lead, another department—usually chemistry—was involved as well. By contrast, when the chemistry department took the lead, other departments—generally biology—only played a part in roughly one in twenty cases.

The number of items per case was typically fairly small. In 74 per cent, ten items or less were submitted by the police to the FSS. In a further 15 per cent there were between 11 and 20 items, while only in 11 per cent were there more than 20 items. Biology department cases tended to consist of greater numbers of items than did chemistry ones: 42 per cent of cases where the biology department took the lead involved over ten items, as opposed to a mere 16 per cent of chemistry department cases. This suggests, perhaps, that biology cases—bearing in mind also the greater frequency with which they were referred to other departments for additional assistance—were of greater complexity than chemistry ones. (An added complication was that, among the batches of cases submitted by each of the four police forces, the proportion of biology cases varied between as much as 33 per cent in Derbyshire and 49 per cent in West Midlands, although so far as the two laboratories were concerned these differences tended to even out.)

Biology cases tended to consume larger numbers of manhours than chemistry ones, as is shown by table 3. Here, information was obtained by asking the reporting officers—the scientists personally responsible for the cases—to estimate how much time they themselves devoted to each of their own cases; in addition, they were also asked to estimate how much time other staff spent on these cases.

In a clear majority of cases—56 per cent of the 213 biology cases, and 61 per cent of the 321 chemistry cases—the reporting officer spent only a day, or just part of a day, of his own time. Less than ten per cent both of biology and of chemistry cases took four days or longer of the reporting officer's time. In general, more manhours were expended on cases by the junior scientific staff than by the reporting officers. Nevertheless, over a third of the biology cases and almost half the chemistry ones were estimated to have taken only one day or less of the time of other scientific staff.

Table 3
Reporting officers' estimates of the amount of time spent on cases

	Days per case, biology department (n = 213)		Days per case, chemistry department (n = 321)	
	Reporting officers	Other scientists	Reporting officers	Other scientists
	%	%	%	%
Day (or part)	56	34	61	48
2–3 days	34	42	30	38
4–10 days	8	18	9	11
10 days (up)	2	4	—	2
Uncertain	—	1	—	1
Total	100	100	100	100

Notes
1. This table is concerned with the time actually devoted to individual cases, translated into notional working days. Turn-around time between the arrival of exhibits at the laboratory and the completion of the scientific report was generally a matter of weeks rather than days.
2. Setting the single-day cases against all those which took longer, and looking separately at the periods of time spent by reporting officers and by other scientific staff, the difference between the biology cases and chemistry ones is statistically significant only for the other scientific staff, and not for the reporting officers $(p < .05)$.

There was a slight difference between the two laboratories in the time devoted to cases. Reporting officers at Huntingdon dealt with 57 per cent of their cases in a single day, as opposed to a higher level of 61 per cent for Birmingham; and while the Huntingdon reporting officers cleared 88 per cent of their cases in three days, those at Birmingham dealt with 93 per cent in the same timespan. But it would be unwise to make much of this difference. Certainly there was no such contrast between the two laboratories for the time spent on cases by other scientific staff. Overall, taking account of the time which both reporting officers and those helping them devoted to the cases, the personnel of each of the two laboratories seem to have allocated fairly similar amounts of time to their respective cases.

3 How far the FSS helped the police

This chapter seeks to quantify the value of the FSS to the police. It is based almost entirely on information drawn from the 330 questionnaires administered to police investigating officers. When fieldwork was being carried out, neither the scientists nor the research team were aware of the ultimate outcome of cases, and so were only able to make educated guesses about the contribution of the FSS to the work of the police and the courts.

Initial impact of FSS reports on the police investigations

The key questions put to investigating officers called for a blend of fact and opinion. They were asked to balance the value of the forensic evidence against the other evidence they had managed to assemble. There was a sequence of questions as to whether the FSS report had strengthened or upheld the case against a suspect (either charged or uncharged); whether it had led to charges being brought; and whether it had fully cleared someone of suspicion. The officers' answers were supplemented by their responses to further questions in those cases which had been without suspects—where, in other words, the FSS was contacted in order to define the nature of the supposed offence. The results are set out in table 1. This shows that there

Table 1
Primary outcome of FSS report for police investigation

	Cases with uncharged suspects	Cases with charged suspects	Cases without suspects	Total
OUTCOME	%	%	%	%
Contributed to prosecution evidence	39	76	n.a.	46
Suspect fully cleared	14	<1	n.a.	5
Helped define nature of case	n.a.	n.a.	82	18
No contribution	47	23	18	30
	100%	100%	100%	100%
n =	117	140	73	330

was a clearly negative outcome in only 30 per cent of cases, although that proportion varied quite substantially for each of the three mutually exclusive groups, reaching its highest level—nearly half—for cases involving uncharged suspects. By contrast, in over three-quarters of the cases where a suspect had been charged, the FSS contributed additional evidence to the prosecution. Where there was no suspect, the FSS shed some fresh light on the offence— defining its nature more clearly than before—in as many as 82 per cent of cases. Finally, there was a total of 5 per cent of cases where the main consequence of the forensic analysis was to clear someone completely, usually a suspect who had not actually been charged.

It is helpful, first, to look at the 73 cases without suspects, before concentrating in greater detail on the other more numerous ones. This rather awkward set of cases, the outcome of which is difficult to classify with any real precision, included a few instances where the identity of the 'offender' was not in doubt but additional information was required to establish the nature of the offence (e.g. in terms of the blood-alcohol level of an assailant or victim at the time the crime was committed). The largest group—over a third of the 73 cases—were suspected arsons, where the police contacted the FSS to discover whether the fire had been started deliberately and, if so, how. In most cases the FSS managed to provide information which the police found helpful, although its effect was often merely to confirm the need for a police investigation, rather than to point to a culprit with an unusual *modus operandi*. The cases other than arson covered a wide range and the contributions of the FSS were, accordingly, varied.

Details of the 257 cases where a suspect, whether charged or uncharged, had been identified before referral to the FSS, and where the object of referral was to confirm and strengthen the thrust of the investigation, are presented in table 2. This table allows a clear distinction to be drawn between those cases where the FSS assisted the police investigation and those where it had no effect. The FSS helped the investigation in just over a third of those cases with suspects. Cases where the FSS had a positive effect are divided into six categories (accounting for almost two-thirds overall). Those with uncharged suspects, where the forensic report had pointed to charges (with a greater or lesser degree of force), only comprised 18 per cent of the total and, in some of these, charges were not actually brought, for various reasons. (Either the total amount of evidence assembled by the police was never adequate to sustain a prosecution, despite the forensic contribution, or else there was an unexpected development, such as the suspect killing himself, or a key witness refusing to testify.) Cases involving suspects who had been charged, and where the work of the FSS strengthened the police action, accounted for a much larger proportion of the total—42 per cent. The last group of cases is made up of those where the report fully cleared either a suspect or someone who had been charged: together, these accounted for 7 per cent.

Table 2
Primary outcome of FSS report for police investigation (excluding cases without suspects)

	No.	%
EFFECT ON UNCHARGED PERSONS (n = 117)		
Person charged wholly/largely as result of report	20	8 ⎫
Person charged partly/marginally as result of report	8	3 ⎬ 18%
Charges not brought (despite supportive report)	18	7 ⎭
Person fully cleared (ie exculpation)	16	6
Suspicions not upheld (ie no contribution)	55	21 = negative outcome
EFFECT ON CHARGED PERSONS (n = 140)		
Case strengthened/upheld	107	42
Charged person fully cleared	1	<1
Case not strengthened/upheld	32	12 = negative outcome
The two negative outcomes	87	34
All six other outcomes	170	66
Total	257	100

Notes
1. All percentages are of the total figure of 257.
2. Suspects/charged persons include those suspected/charged at any time up to the writing of the report. The small number of cases where the police only wanted information about the nature of the supposed offence, rather than to confirm the identity of an offender, have been excluded from this table, which is a reconstituted version of part of the previous table, presented in greater detail.

Although the rest of this chapter will mainly be concerned with cases where the forensic report strengthened the pre-existing direction of the police investigation, it is important to look in some detail at the 17 cases where someone was exonerated. There were in fact an additional four cases where one person was cleared of suspicion at the same time as the case against another person was strengthened, giving an overall total of 21 exoneration cases. However, the 17 cases without clear alternative suspects presented the greatest danger—had not the forensic report indicated otherwise—that innocent suspects might conceivably have been put on trial.

In one case, charges had actually been brought before the FSS was contacted. The owner of a restaurant had made a citizen's arrest after one of a group of youths had broken a window. The FSS report, which showed that there were no glass particles on the youth's clothes, confirmed the investigating officer's suspicion that the restaurateur had arrested the wrong person. In some of the other exculpation cases, although charges had not formally been laid, the evidence against the suspect—pending the FSS report—seemed quite

19

strong. In one instance, involving the rape of a woman in her home, the principal suspect was a man with ready access to the house who was actually identified by the rape victim; but he proved to be of the wrong blood group (and eventually someone else was arrested, who pleaded guilty). In another case, after a robbery at a hotel, some youths were found in possession of masks and other equipment used in the raid: the FSS report upheld their claim—originally viewed with scepticism by some officers—that they were innocent, and had only just found the equipment, quite by chance (almost a year later the police caught up with the actual culprits).

Given that eye-witnesses can make mistakes, and that police officers can sometimes be misled, the FSS clearly has an intermittent but vital role to play in protecting the innocent, as well as in strengthening the case against those who commit offences. On occasion, it can also help to reduce the numbers of a small pool of suspects, as happened in the four cases where one person was cleared but one or more other people were incriminated.

Police ratings

Police officers were asked not only to estimate the impact of the forensic report on the cases for which they were responsible but also to rate the value of the FSS contribution on a seven-point scale. Because the benefits of referring a case to the FSS tended to be indirect or uncertain for those investigations without a suspect, the results of the ratings questions are best presented—as in table 3—both for all 330 cases in the police sample and also, separately, for cases with and without suspects, when the FSS was first contacted.

Table 3 reveals that the proportion of cases with a favourable rating— crucial, substantial or useful—ranged between 56 per cent (for cases with suspects) to 24 per cent (for the much smaller set of cases without a suspect), and was roughly half of all 330. In those cases where a suspect had been identified, the investigating officers did not find it too difficult to make a clear judgement. However, in over half the 68 cases where no suspect had been identified—where the whole investigation had often proved difficult— the police officer found it hard to say precisely what the contribution of the FSS had been. Where definite assessments were made for these 68 cases, they were evenly split between, on the one hand, a crucial or substantial or useful marking, and, on the other hand, one of minimal, little or no help.

The police investigations: developments after forensic analysis

Roughly two out of three cases in the police sample were ultimately recorded as cleared up, almost double the average national clearance rate for 1984. In those cases where the FSS contribution was favourably assessed (ratings of

Table 3
Police officers' assessments of the contribution made by the FSS to their investigations

Police ratings	Cases where suspect was known		Cases without known suspect		All cases	
	%		%		%	
Crucial	12 ⎫		1 ⎫		9 ⎫	
Substantial	22 ⎬ 56%		10 ⎬ 24%		19 ⎬ 49%	
Useful	23 ⎭		12 ⎭		20 ⎭	
Minimal/little	12 ⎫ 41%		15 ⎫ 24%		13 ⎫ 37%	
No help	29 ⎭		9 ⎭		25 ⎭	
Uncertain	3		53		13	
	100		100		100	
n =	262		68		330	

Notes
1. Cases where a suspect was known include those where charges had been brought. The cut-off point was when the police first contacted the FSS.
2. This table is based on questions 9 and 35 of the police questionnaire.

useful/substantial/crucial) as many as 79 per cent were cleared up, whereas the equivalent figure for those less favourably assessed was only 52 per cent. Because—as pointed out in the previous chapter—the police not infrequently turned to the FSS as a last resort, it is scarcely surprising that, in almost half the 104 cases where the forensic report failed to support the prevailing thrust of an investigation, the police discontinued their enquiries altogether.

Ultimately, of the 330 cases, there were 150 (45 per cent) in which someone was convicted. Of these 150, only 27 involved contested trials (over three-quarters of them in the Crown Court); in the remaining 123 cases the offender simply pleaded guilty. These figures do not include the 15 instances in which someone was acquitted, or had their case dismissed, and would probably have increased very slightly if the research team had waited longer before interviewing the police. Looking first at the 123 uncontested trials, nearly two-thirds of the investigating officers felt that a guilty plea would have been likely even without the forensic evidence. This verdict is however a little at odds with the findings already presented and needs to be treated with some caution, in that the officers were being asked to speculate about the motives of someone with whom they may have had relatively little personal contact.

Turning to the smaller group of 27 contested trials resulting in convictions—where the relative contribution of different types of evidence was much more clearly exposed—forensic evidence was deployed by the prosecution in 21 cases. Either the report alone was presented or the FSS reporting officer also gave evidence from the witness stand. The investigating officers thought that the forensic evidence had played an essential or important part in nine cases; that it had been useful in a further nine; and that it had only been of low value, or unhelpful to the prosecution, in the other three cases. So the forensic evidence contributed helpfully to the prosecution in two-thirds of the 27 contested trials resulting in convictions.

Contrasts between police forces

The extent to which different police forces use their local laboratory varies widely. Bedfordshire and West Midlands refer cases at, respectively, roughly twice the rate of Essex and Derbyshire (see chapter 1). While the two forces with high referral rates have more crimes per officer to investigate than the other two forces, this by itself is insufficient to explain the difference. Force policy on referrals to the FSS may account for part of the discrepancy, or different working practices may have arisen as a result of such factors as the distance between police forces and laboratories. (The latter point is one which could apply both to Derbyshire and Essex.) Individual police forces decide for themselves how often to turn to the FSS. (The relevant local authorities are charged for this annually, as a component of Common Police Services, at a rate determined by the size of the force.) Do those forces which make high use of the FSS manage to get as good a return on their investment as those making comparatively little use of the FSS: or do the high-use forces suffer from diminishing returns?

The conclusion from this research, based both on officers' views and on more objective outcome measures, is that the two high-use forces (Bedfordshire, West Midlands) actually got a better rate of return on their investment than the two low-use forces (Derbyshire, Essex). There was no sign—at these referral levels—that diminishing returns were beginning to apply. On the contrary, the high-use forces seemed to gain slightly more from their local laboratory; if this reflects superior referral skills, these could have arisen from greater familiarity with the FSS.

Although the high-use forces obtained better results from referrals to the FSS than the low-use ones, the point should not be over-stated. As illustrated in table 4, the difference is only a modest one, and the attitudinal ratings could be affected by a variety of factors other than the outcome of the laboratories' work. On the one hand, for example, the perceived value of forensic evidence may be reduced where other evidence is abundant. On the other hand, police attitudes to the value of forensic evidence may be positively influenced by the mere fact that it is force policy to make high use of the FSS's services. For what it is worth, therefore, the FSS contribution was rated as useful, substantial or crucial by 63 per cent of officers from high-use forces, as opposed to an equivalent figure of only 51 per cent for the low-use forces. This difference is statistically significant ($p < .05$).

22

Table 4
Police ratings of FSS contribution, in high-use and low-use forces

Officers' ratings	Forces making high use of FSS		Forces making low use of FSS	
	No.	%	No.	%
Crucial, substantial or useful	90	63	73	51
Minimal, little or no help	53	37	70	49
Total	143	100	143	100

Notes
1. The 44 cases where the police officers were uncertain as to how to evaluate the FSS contribution (21 for the low-use forces and 23 for the high-use forces, generally cases without suspects) have been excluded from this table, which is based on question 35 of the police questionnaire (and question 2 of the main questionnaire).
2. The difference is statistically significant (chi squared = 4.12, $P < .05$).

This contrast between high-use and low-use forces is apparently genuine, in that comparable sorts of cases were submitted by the two pairs of forces. A suspect had been identified just as often in both sets of offences. This is important, since cases with suspects were significantly more likely to result in favourable ratings of the work of the FSS than those without them; in this key respect, the two pairs of forces gave the FSS comparable material with which to work. While the high-use forces submitted a higher proportion of biology cases than the low-use ones (46 per cent as opposed to 34 per cent), this can only have had a marginal effect—as will be discussed at a later point in this chapter.

Several factors, none of them individually conclusive, suggest that the high-use forces contrived to get a little more value out of the FSS. For instance, while the total numbers of murders and rapes were similar for the two pair of forces, five of the six cases in the police sample where the courts imposed a sentence of life imprisonment or a term of at least ten years were from high-use forces. In three of those five cases the forensic contribution was given a high rating by the investigating officer (useful or substantial). In other words, the FSS input proved particularly helpful to the high-use forces in facilitating the successful prosecution of major offenders.

The FSS report strengthened or upheld the case against a suspect—either charged or uncharged—in a higher proportion of cases for high-use than for low-use forces. This difference was slight, and did not reach statistical significance (of the 330 cases, 83 out of the 166 from high-use forces— exactly 50 per cent—were strengthened, as against 70 out of 164 for the low-use forces, or 43 per cent).

23

A further contrast—which, if still relatively modest, was statistically significant ($p < .05$)—between the two groups, occurred in the 123 cases where the suspect pleaded guilty. Of these, 62 were from high-use forces, and 61 were from the low-use ones. In 30 per cent of the former group, the investigating officer reckoned that this admission of culpability would have been either highly unlikely or at least fairly unlikely without the forensic evidence. The equivalent figure for the cases from the low-use forces was only 13 per cent.

Similarly interesting, although not by itself conclusive, is the use made of forensic evidence at the 21 contested trials in which forensic evidence was presented by the prosecution. In all, 14 of these were from high-use forces, in every single one of which the investigating officer rated the forensic evidence as having been useful, important or essential to the prosecution. Only in four of the seven contested cases from low-use forces involving forensic evidence was an equally favourable assessment made by the police.

In successive stages of the investigation and trial process, the forces making comparatively high use of the FSS apparently managed to squeeze a little extra mileage out of the scientists' efforts. The difference was qualitative as well as merely quantitative, and although it was never particularly large, it is clear that the high-use forces were capable of doing every bit as well—if not slightly better—than the low-use forces, out of their respective referrals of cases to the FSS. The high-use forces had a slightly more impressive clear-up rate (70 per cent) than that for the low-use forces (60 per cent). However, while this difference may have arisen partly from the ability of the high-use forces to gain a bit more from the cases which they referred to the FSS, it fell just short of being statistically significant. Even if the high-use forces did not do strikingly better than the low-use ones out of their referrals, they certainly did well enough to justify their higher usage of the FSS.

The underlying assumption in this section has been that the FSS provided a standard level of service, whether operating from Birmingham or from Huntingdon. In this context it is relevant to note that each laboratory served both a high-use and a low-use force. What small difference emerged between the laboratories in terms of police ratings of performance may well be attributable to side-effects of the difficulties engendered by 'the Fox' case for the Huntingdon laboratory (the relevant time-series analysis forms part of Appendix C). After allowing for the disruptive consequences of this case, the remaining difference between the two laboratories is scarcely out of line with the fairly comparable amounts of time devoted to cases by the staff of each of the two laboratories (see chapter 2).

Contrasts between laboratory departments and types of crime

Within each laboratory, the biology department (40 per cent of cases) was concerned mainly with offences against the person, while chemistry (57 per cent of cases) dealt largely with offences against property. The work of the

24

chemistry departments at the two laboratories strengthened the case against a suspect (charged or uncharged) slightly more often than that of the biology department. However, when judged by the overall ratings of the investigating officers, this small difference disappears: roughly half of both biology and chemistry cases were assessed as having made a useful, substantial or crucial contribution. The biology department was also especially helpful in dealing with some very serious offences—murders and rapes—and these were among the cases where the high-use forces got particularly good results from their use of the FSS. But, in general, both departments handled a mixed range of offences, some where they were able to be very helpful to the police and others less so.

While there was little in the way of any general contrast between the work of the two main laboratory departments, rather more clear-cut differences emerged between the various sorts of offences. Table 5 shows that in some

Table 5
The extent to which the FSS contributed to the investigation of cases in different offence categories

Offence category (and number of cases per category)	Case strengthened against suspect (or charged person)	Police had favourable view of FSS assistance
	%	%
Violence (62)	65	65
Sexual (55)	24	36
Burglary (79)	54	52
Robbery (12)	17	42
Theft (40)	73	73
Damage (76)	33	34
Fraud/other (6)	17	33

Notes
1. The total number of cases shown is 330. A "favourable view" was one where the FSS contribution was rated as useful, substantial or crucial.
2. This table is based on questions 30 and 35 of the police questionnaire, and on question 3 of the data collection form.

offence categories the work of the FSS was notably more productive, and more favourably assessed by the investigating officers, than in others. Of the seven categories, four contained more than 50 cases: violence, sexual offences, burglaries and damage. Together, these four categories of offence accounted for 272 cases, or 82 per cent of the total. Violence and burglary were the success stories; results were poorer for the sexual offences and damage. This set of outcomes may have played a part in building up the overall advantage gained by the high-use forces over the low-use ones. The high-use forces submitted proportionately more cases of violence and burglary, and also comparatively fewer ones of sexual offences and damage, than the low-use forces. Yet, the high-use forces did not get better results just in one or two individual offence categories: they did a little better right across the board.

In the two substantial categories with good results—violence and burglary—the suspect's identity was known in as many as nine cases out of ten. The same was true of the smaller group of thefts, where the work of the FSS was often fruitful (in 73 per cent of such cases, as measured either way). In the sex and damage cases, where the scientists' results were more disappointing, there was less often a suspect who had been identified: between five and seven cases out of ten. While a positive outcome, however defined, was much more likely where a suspect had been identified, investigating officers sometimes had other reasons for enlisting FSS help than strengthening the evidence against a known person. They wanted to learn, for instance, whether a fire had actually involved arson, and how it might have started; or whether there was proof that a rape or a sexual assault had taken place.

The relative numbers of cases belonging to different offence categories played a part in determining the effectiveness of the work of the FSS; so also did the extent to which a suspect had been identified, and each of these factors was related to the other. But neither between them nor in combination with other quantifiable factors do they fully explain the outcome of that work. In ways which are hard to pinpoint, some police officers seem to have been more adept than others at exploiting physical evidence.

4 Police and scientists as partners

Having presented evidence as to the effectiveness of the FSS, this chapter proceeds to examine the views and practices of the police and the scientists, and the way they interacted. Much of the material is drawn from the comments of police investigating officers, who were asked their general opinions of the FSS and of the use which police make of it. Occasional use is made of the researchers' own impressions.

The FSS as seen by the police

The 330 cases where police were interviewed were handled by 263 different investigating officers, nearly three-quarters of them from the CID. (The number of detectives involved would have been higher had not many of them been responsible for more than one case.) From a checklist of about a dozen items relating to the FSS, there was only one—the overall usefulness of the Service—on which most 263 interviewees felt able to comment. (The lack of response to the other items stemmed from officers' lack of knowledge about the FSS and consequent unwillingness to comment.) Their verdict was highly favourable. Nearly half of them (48 per cent) rated the FSS as very useful, while a further 37 per cent felt it was fairly useful; only 10 per cent thought the FSS was not particularly useful, while a further 6 per cent were uncertain. A larger proportion of officers from the two forces making high use of the FSS—Bedfordshire and West Midlands—rated the FSS as very useful (53 per cent as opposed to 42 per cent in Derbyshire and Essex).

This generally enthusiastic endorsement verged on awe for some officers. One referred to a widespread belief among the police that the FSS "can wave a magic wand and get results from anything". Another said that the FSS was the only organisation he had never heard being criticised by fellow officers. Officers frequently commented that the FSS would continue to grow in importance. There were a good many references to the mounting significance of the Police and Criminal Evidence Act, while at least one officer spoke of "criminals no longer confessing and juries becoming reluctant to believe police evidence", and the suggestion was also made that "fingerprint evidence is becoming more difficult to get."

27

However, the approval with which a good many officers viewed the FSS had as its counterpart substantial ignorance, verging on apprehension. (The attitude of the police to the FSS in some ways parallels popular feelings about information technology.) Even though the 263 respondents had all used the FSS at least once, there was a persistent sense of unease. One officer, who believed that greater use would be made of the FSS if the police were better informed, commented that his local laboratory was "like a cloak and dagger place". Another felt that "the whole business of going to a laboratory is a daunting task"—with travelling and parking problems to sort out, the need to prove one's identity, and so on. Detectives who never even went to the laboratory were also prone to anxieties. One said he was "hesitant to send things to the lab in case you're laughed at". Another explained that his more junior colleagues "were reluctant even to phone police liaison"—the small group of officers attached to each laboratory, all of them of the rank of sergeant or above—still less the scientists themselves. The latter were widely seen as remote, mysterious and over-burdened specialists: "far too busy". Indeed, some of the less experienced officers were completely unaware that they could, if necessary, make personal contact with the member of the FSS handling their own case, although more senior officers and members of specialist squads prided themselves on their ability to establish good working relationships with the scientists.

Only 30 per cent of officers felt able to comment on communications between police and scientists; they were fairly evenly divided between those who were satisfied and those who were critical. Even fewer—14 per cent—commented on police liaison, and of these roughly two out of three made adverse comments. In both contexts, senior officers were more likely to be content with current arrangements than were junior ones. Perhaps this was because, in the words of one interviewee, "there's a lot of liaison between scientists and senior officers, but they don't talk to the officers who are actually doing the job." One junior officer went so far as to talk of "a complete breakdown in communications with the laboratory". There were quite a few complaints about the inadequacy of information coming from the FSS, and the difficulty of getting to see round the laboratory. Adverse comments about the police liaison staff hinged around their tendency "to put up barriers between you and the scientists", and at the variable way they rejected some exhibits on arrival at the laboratory (especially when checking that the case was one where forensic evidence was genuinely required, and that a confession had not been made).

Over a third of the officers discussed the extent to which the police were informed about the FSS, and of these fewer than one in ten were satisfied. "The majority of officers are completely in the dark" about the FSS, was one officer's assessment. While this point was felt to apply, in particular, to uniformed officers, the suggestion was also made that "there are CID officers who aren't aware of the full service they [the FSS] provide." It was thus scarcely surprising that members of the research team found themselves answering as well as asking questions. On one occasion even a Detective Inspector wanted to know whether or not the FSS could assess footprints from photographs as opposed to casts.

Apart from the widely perceived need for both FSS and police to provide, between them, better information and training, only one specific element of the FSS incurred significant criticism by the officers. This was the documents department, which forms part of the Birmingham laboratory. This department examines signatures and other handwritten, typewritten or documentary evidence, for the whole of England and Wales (except London). Nearly a third of police interviewees mentioned this section of the FSS; four out of five who did so were critical—often fiercely so. Comments as scathing as "total waste of time" or "they never give a straight answer so I never bother with them now" were not unusual. The study of handwriting may not be so rigorous a science as chemical or biological analysis, but this does not fully explain why there should have been quite such vehement dissatisfaction. Cases handled by the documents department were excluded from the research sample, thus making it hard to get to the root of the problem, or to assess it other than in strictly provisional terms, yet it seems that this too may, at least in part, reflect a deficiency in communications and training. The handwriting specialists need substantially more than the odd signature or a few specimen lines of writing if they are to contribute effectively to a case— a point of which not all officers were fully aware. Interestingly, the two interviewees with experience of specialist fraud or cheque squad work were prominent among the smaller group of officers who were pleased with the work of the documents department.

Investigating the scene of the crime—the problem of contamination

An important focus of interaction between the FSS and the police is the way exhibits are forwarded to laboratories by the police. The research sheds light on some of the difficulties involved. The process begins with the retrieval of evidence from the scene of the crime, or from victims and suspects; this is done mainly by uniformed officers, detectives and SOCOs (Scenes of Crime Officers—roughly a quarter of these are now civilians), together with doctors. Of the 330 cases in the police sample, detectives were most frequently involved in locating evidence (in 52 per cent of cases), followed by SOCOs (39 per cent), doctors (27 per cent) and uniformed officers (26 per cent). It was often a joint effort.

In a good many cases where SOCOs attended the scene, SOCO and investigating officer would assess it jointly, and decide between them what to select for forensic analysis. The value of the evidence gathered was sometimes highly dependent on the skill of the SOCOs, as police and scientists were well aware. On the whole, SOCOs were respected for their special expertise, although there were some suggestions of a conflict of interest between SOCO and investigating officer, or that SOCOs were being trained in scenes-of-crime work at the expense of detectives. In one case—resulting in criticism at court and in disciplinary procedures—the SOCO failed to notice key exhibits, and damaged some of those which he did not collect.

In gathering, packaging, storing or transporting evidence, the great danger is that of contamination: allowing items submitted for matching to come into contact with each other before forensic analysis. FSS files suggested the possibility of contamination in 3 per cent of all 593 cases. Of the 330 cases where the investigating officer was interviewed, and specifically asked about this point, scope for contamination was mentioned by the officers in a slightly higher proportion of cases: 5 per cent. While these officers were willing to admit to the possibility of contamination when the question was put to them in person, not all of them had informed the FSS of the potential hazard.

How did the risk of contamination arise? One example—which only came to light at court—concerned a burglary at a football supporters' club where entry had been made by smashing a window, and some beer had been taken. The police found the stolen beer at the house of a man living nearby, and forensic analysis matched three fragments of glass from the suspect's clothes to the broken window. However—unknown to the forensic scientist—the detective in charge of the investigation had gone to the suspect's house fresh from visiting the scene of the burglary and, in court, the defence argued that the glass fragments might inadvertently have been shed by the officer. The upshot was that the judge ordered the forensic evidence to be excluded, and the suspect was acquitted. In other cases, the FSS was aware of the possibility of contamination, and took corrective action. The initial screening of exhibits which are inadequately packaged or in some other way potentially contaminated is one of the duties of the police liaison staff at the laboratories; this means that conspicuously unsuitable exhibits are rejected outright, and would therefore have been excluded from the scope of the research.

Scientists handling the cases sometimes took the initiative themselves. For instance, in the case of a theft of car components, involving possible fibre transfer from the suspect's clothing, the scientist surmised from the HOLAB form that the same officer might have handled both the clothing and the car parts. He telephoned the investigating officer, who proved unaware of the danger of contamination but, as it happened, had dealt with the two sets of items at different times. The scientist, sufficiently reassured, continued with his examination, which confirmed the fibre transfer; subsequently the suspect pleaded guilty, though the police officer was uncertain whether or not the scientist's report had helped to bring about this outcome. There were other cases where the scientists restricted the scope of their examination, as opposed to accepting or rejecting the case as a whole. For example, in one case

30

involving various types of evidence, the scientist did not examine any of the items for glass because the control sample had been 'packed' in a brown paper bag, and might have come into contact with other exhibits.

The full extent of the problem of contamination—especially for uniform branch—became apparent in general discussions with the 263 police interviewees. Of the 72 officers (27 per cent) who raised this issue, approximately one in ten felt confident that enough was being done to educate uniformed officers. The remainder were critical, if not despairing. As one detective lamented, "the bobby on the beat, if he arrives first [at the scene of the crime], is apt to stamp over everything", adding that he himself, when he had been in uniform, had done precisely the same. While taking charge of scenes of crime, uniformed officers may well find themselves gathering items of evidence (in cases which, later, are generally taken over by the CID) and, to an increasing extent, may even assume responsibility for the whole investigation process. However, a substantial number of uniformed interviewees maintained that they had never been told anything about contamination. One was under the impression that avoiding contamination meant simply protecting oneself from contagious diseases, by wearing rubber gloves. Another, so the researcher who interviewed him noted, was "quite surprised and interested" when some of the possible dangers were explained to him.

Problems of contamination are highlighted in various courses given by the FSS to police officers, particularly members of the CID; nevertheless, ignorance of contamination was widely acknowledged to be a deeply-rooted problem. Officers offering solutions tended to favour brief, practical courses: a day's training, or two at most. Even senior officers and CID personnel would benefit, or so some interviewees believed. The problem of contamination was one which affected all four forces to a limited extent, although half of the total of 16 cases (out of 330) came from West Midlands. In addition, the proportion of interviewees in West Midlands who felt that uniformed officers were insufficiently aware of contamination was higher than in the other three forces (39 per cent as opposed to figures ranging from 11 to 30 per cent). Also, complaints about the lack of proper packaging material at night—when offenders are active, yet SOCOs are off-duty—were especially common in West Midlands.

Furthermore, it was in West Midlands that the process of interviewing brought to light a slip-up in the investigation of a crime scene. Outside a burgled house, a civilian photographer, who had been asked by a police officer to take a picture of a shoeprint, apparently left by the offender, inadvertently photographed a mark left by someone else. None of the officers involved in the case, nor the relevant scientist, suspected that anything was wrong until matters became clear at the interview—although the scientist had been well aware that the shoeprint in the photograph bore no resemblance at all to the suspect's shoes, as he had duly stated in his report.

31

If accidents could and did happen, there was no sign of any deliberate planting or tampering with evidence in any of the cases studied. The whole question of planted evidence was raised by a few police interviewees, whose contention was that the forensic scientists were occasionally over-zealous in guarding against this, and simply rejected out of hand items which were too obviously or too crudely associated. Perhaps allegations of this kind are best seen as backhanded compliments to the scientists on their neutrality.

In the small group of cases where the scientist attended the scene of the crime in person, at least some of the dangers involved in dealing with physical evidence were minimised. There were just 28 such cases out of the 547 about which scientists were interviewed. In 20 out of the 28 instances, the scientists were summoned by the police to investigate suspected arsons. This was due to the need to identify the seat of the fire, before evidential material could usefully be collected—often an extremely difficult matter. On two out of three occasions when the FSS report cast doubt on the local fire brigade's analysis, a visit to the scene had been necessary. The eight visits to scenes other than fires involved a wide variety of serious or complicated offences. The view of the scientists was that visits saved them time in the long run, by giving a better insight into cases and reducing the amount of evidence to be examined, while improving its potential value. In all but two of the 28 cases, they felt their visit to have been worthwhile.

A few visits to crime scenes led to sustained participation by the scientist in the investigation. For instance, shortly after the body of a prostitute had been found, strangled with her bra, a scientist was called to the scene. He was able to help ensure the preservation of the body, and to safeguard vital physical evidence such as used contraceptives and tyremarks. Later, the scientist attended successive conferences organised by the investigating officer, giving whatever advice he could as various suspects came to the attention of the police. Although the crime remained unsolved, the investigating officer praised the scientist's endeavours, and said that, with hindsight, he would have called in the scientist straightaway, instead of waiting until an hour or so after the body had been found.

The laboratory phase—communications between scientists and police

Usually, the scientist would go to work guided only by the brief details written in the HOLAB form. The police submitted copies of written statements by witnesses, or other such documents, in less than ten per cent of cases. Limited as the amount of information provided by the police may have been, the scientists were usually content with this, although in 16 per cent (of their 547 cases) they stated that insufficient information had been provided. In virtually all these instances they had asked the police to make good the deficiency, and this was generally done. The scientists sometimes found it difficult to extract such information although, as one of them put it, "in a complicated case I would expect to have to clarify details on one or two matters." The job specifications—the lists of specific tasks for each case referred to the FSS—on which the scientists also gave their views, were considered satisfactory over nine times out of ten.

Sometimes the purpose of the scientists' work would change in mid-case. In 8 per cent of all 593 cases there were important developments in the police investigation—of which the laboratory was informed—while scientific analysis was still in progress. For instance, new suspects might have come to the attention of the police, or a suspect or witness or victim might have changed his or her account of the incident. In a larger, partly overlapping group, accounting for 14 per cent of the cases, additional items of evidence were submitted to the laboratory; in some of these the police took the initiative, while in others it was the scientist or was planned jointly between them.

Before writing his report, the scientist was in contact with the police, for one reason or another, in almost half the cases. In theory, the police liaison officers at each of the laboratories were generally supposed to act as intermediaries between investigating officers and scientists, but more often than not they were by-passed. Contact was most often made by phone; although the scientists were required to keep a brief record of all telephone calls with the police on a special form, no analysis of these was carried out by the research team.

Where personal contact was established, relations between scientists and police were generally amicable and untroubled. In all but eight of the 330 cases covered by the police questionnaires, the investigating officer stated that the FSS had done what was asked of it. Cases where the investigating officer was dissatisfied were mostly those where not all the items were examined or, alternatively, where the analysis was insufficiently detailed. A few police interviewees complained more generally about the increasing tendency of the FSS—for reasons of economy—not to examine all the items submitted; this was felt to weaken the effectiveness of the scientist's work, and even, as a few officers asserted, to have had a disastrous impact on some contested trials.

When investigating officers had a strong interest in any particular type of analysis, this seems generally to have been carried out, if only after discussion on the telephone. Providing there was no suggestion of contamination, the FSS was reluctant to challenge specific requests by investigating officers. There was, however, the odd occasion when, even after taking on a case, the FSS asked the police "to establish good reasons for requesting time-consuming examination without more policework." The FSS, in keeping with the current emphasis on obtaining value for money, was making increasing efforts to scrutinise cases, not only to check that the police needed forensic assistance (because a guilty plea could not be counted on), but also to make sure that the police possessed other evidence to complement any forensic findings. For example, at Huntingdon, after an unusually large

33

group of cases was submitted for analysis of bloodstains found at the scene of burglaries where no suspects had been traced, the laboratory made it clear that it would cease to carry out any analysis in such circumstances. Withdrawal of this service raised hardly any regrets among the investigating officers interviewed in Bedfordshire and Essex, perhaps because they were aware of the pressure of other demands on the FSS; but Scenes of Crime Officers may have regretted the loss of this service because it may, in their view, have prevented connections being made with different scenes of burglary where there were suspects.

The report and its impact

The report or statement is the usual end-product of the scientist's work: a slender document, but written with considerable care. Only in 24 cases out of the 547 covered by scientists' questionnaires (4 per cent) did the scientist actually appear in court, where he was able to give a personal presentation while being cross-questioned.

Prepared by an expert for the benefit of police officers, lawyers, defendants, jury members and other non-scientists, the report is an inherently awkward document to compile. It has to be easy to understand. It has to be as precise as possible. And it also has to be scrupulously correct: beyond challenge from any other expert. The great concern of the FSS in recent years with quality assurance is strongly reflected in the cautious composition of reports; some efforts have also been made to foster the composition of clearer reports. The scientist who is responsible for the case writes by hand a first draft which is then checked and endorsed, point by point, by a senior member of staff. Only when any doubtful aspects are clarified is a final typewritten version produced and sent off to the police.

Two-thirds of the 87 police interviewees who mentioned the reports said that they found them vague or obscure. There was even a small group of officers who felt that scientists, when in court, were more positive than they were on paper, although in theory there should never be any discrepancy between the weight of a scientist's evidence given orally and in writing. This is likely to be due to the greater impact of spoken testimony and the scientist's response to unlikely suggestions made by defence counsel.

On one occasion, two members of the research team saw at first hand how reports may be misinterpreted. The colleague of a detective whom they had been interviewing produced an FSS report—dealing with the transfer of glass particles on to clothing—which he had just received (a copy of the text of this report, which was from a case outside the sample, can be found in Appendix B). In so far as he could understand the report, the detective's initial impression was that it would not help in preparing the case for prosecution. The researchers, asked their opinion, felt that the report was practically conclusive evidence of a transfer, and suggested that a telephone call to the scientist would confirm this—as proved to be so. It is not too difficult to see why this particular report was hard to grasp, although it is neither more nor less clear than many others.

Various interviewees commented that the reports were written in a kind of code or shorthand, and that it was necessary to "read between the lines". The research team, in reading hundreds of these documents, became familiar with their often heavily qualified conclusions, and, like many detectives, grew accustomed to interpreting such phrases as "could have", or just "could", or "consistent with" in the context of the report as a whole. Whether it is reasonable to expect as much of every police officer, or of all those who participate in criminal trials, must be open to doubt.

While it is impossible to quantify, it seems likely that the style of reports led to a blunting of their impact. This question is not a simple one, and can only be approached obliquely. One starting point is to consider how both police and scientists rated the contribution of each report—as first dispatched from the laboratory—to the investigation; they used the same seven-point scale, with similar sets of guidelines. A table presented in Appendix D shows that while their ratings did not vary markedly in nearly two cases out of three, there were noticeable differences (two or more scale points) in the remaining third. Also, at a more detailed level, of the 103 cases where the scientist assessed his contribution as crucial or substantial, the investigating officer rated only just under half of these at the same high points on the scale; there were even 12 where the officer's view was that the report had been no help at all. In some cases at least, there would seem to have been an element of misunderstanding.

Although it is hard to determine the extent to which reports did not get their message across satisfactorily, one suggestive indicator is that while the police graded 49 per cent of cases as useful, substantial or crucial, the equivalent figure for the scientists was slightly higher, at 55 per cent; while that for the researchers, who made similar assessments, was virtually the same as for the scientists, at 54 per cent. Furthermore—in all probability—police officers may not have been alone in experiencing difficulties with the interpretation of reports: quite conceivably, not all prosecuting solicitors and barristers appreciated their full value, nor perhaps all jurors. The research was not able to test this directly. But failure to understand forensic reports may have contributed on the one hand to decision not to prosecute in cases where reports seemed to support prosecution (18 cases fell in this category), and on the other hand to acquittals (there were 15 cases in the sample where the defendant was acquitted). Two further examples of problematic reports are included in Appendix B: in each of these the scientist marked his contribution as crucial, but the investigating officer—despite the existence of additional circumstantial evidence—said the report had not offered sufficiently convincing evidence to sustain a prosecution.

35

The question of possible bias among scientists towards the prosecution needs brief examination. The position is that, in theory, the FSS caters impartially for whoever approaches it—whether the police or the defence—and that it does not allow itself to become too closely identified with either side. In practice, the police alone make use of the FSS, and have, to some extent, a close relationship with it. The FSS does its best to take account of this. However, in over a third of the 43 cases (out of 593) where the police submitted a witness statement or a comparable document along with the exhibits, the scientist made no mention of this in his report, although there is no reason to believe that scientists were swayed in any improper way by reading such documents—which, in some instances, presented the suspect's own account—the need for thoroughgoing openness remains, and is reinforced by a further point. Only in 12 cases (out of their 547) were scientists in contact, before the actual trial, with fellow experts or legal representatives acting for the defence—in stark contrast with the much greater proportion of instances where they were in touch with the police.

Whatever the integrity of FSS staff, this imbalance does pose some awkward questions. Are the right exhibits always examined, and is this done in the ways most appropriate to the defence side as well as to the prevailing thrust of a police investigation? There were even one or two police interviewees who felt that the needs of the defence merited more attention than was customary. However, defence scientists—on the odd occasions when they were called in—did not challenge the competency of the FSS: their role seems merely to have been one of checking, of considering fresh interpretations, and, later on, of briefing barristers before they cross-examined the FSS scientist; all of which was done simply from the one point of view, that of the defence. There is a sense in which the defence scientists can be said to exploit the guardedness, rather than any partisanship, on the part of the FSS. It is certainly a strange situation: the FSS, reserved as it is, has an even less publicly accountable 'shadow', in the shape of a small coterie of scientists who act for the defence side (the largest firm is called "United Kingdom Forensic Science Services", a name closely echoing that of the FSS, from which most of its staff are enticed). Both groups are a charge on the taxpayer; the FSS is funded as part of the Home Office, while fees of the defence scientists are generally paid under the legal aid provisions of the Lord Chancellor's Department. It would however be delicate and possibly expensive to improve present arrangements, given the deeply-rooted nature of the adversarial system of justice in this country.

Certainly far more police officers were greatly concerned about a completely different problem: delay. With cases sometimes taking a month or more for the FSS to process, trial dates occasionally slipped back as a result. The police felt that delay on the part of the FSS had significantly inconvenienced the investigation or prosecution of 8 per cent of cases. A majority of these were from Huntingdon, probably as a result of the heavy demands made on staff there by the many exhibits associated with 'the Fox'. In general discussion with the 263 police officers, roughly four out ten said that delay caused problems. A higher proportion—46 per cent—of officers dependent on Birmingham expressed concern, as opposed to a level of 31 per cent for those relying on Huntingdon. About a quarter of all police interviewees were less worried: "most policemen want an answer yesterday", was an observation which came from one of them. Some officers were content that the FSS could speed up its handling of a case if it were urgent. Many others, however, were still not satisfied, although in a few instances this was because they were unaware of the possibility of a specially accelerated service. Often, those who complained did so not only about the fact that delays happened but also about the uncertainty of knowing how long they would have to wait for reports.

Closing the file

Once the report was written, the case was usually over and the file closed, so far as the FSS was concerned. Only in 5 per cent of their cases did the scientists receive any feedback from the police. There were even fewer occasions where the scientist gave evidence in court. That was one additional way in which, in a further handful of cases, scientists sometimes gleaned information about the outcome of their efforts. Mostly, they had no idea whatsoever of the impact of their work: nor did FSS management.

If communication was limited between the FSS and the police, especially at and after the trial stage, it was also extremely rare for the scientist to be in touch with anyone else—including lawyers acting for the prosecution. In addition to the mere three occasions when the scientist was in contact with legal representatives for the defence before the trial took place, there was a single instance where the scientist conferred with defence counsel in the course of a trial.

In the 4 per cent of cases (24 out of 547) where scientists did not give evidence in court, police interviewees almost invariably spoke highly of their incisiveness and impartiality. Only in their general comments about the handwriting experts did a less favourable view emerge, on occasion, of the scientist as an expert witness. Even then, those who had criticised reports produced by the handwriting experts were sometimes more appreciative of their courtroom performances.

While scientists generally had little involvement in a case once the report had been written and sent to the police, their work, paradoxically, had only just begun to make its mark. The police officer in charge of the investigation had to consider whether or not the report shed fresh light on the offence into which he was enquiring, and whether there was any need for action, such as bringing charges, or preparing a case for prosecution. Just occasionally the officer would telephone the scientist for clarification. The report might be shown to the suspect in the hope of a confession or guilty plea: this could be done personally or, more usually, through a defence solicitor. In a contested case, the report might—and usually would—be served as written evidence. Of all these developments, the scientist would generally know nothing. For him or her, the forensic process was probably over, although its impact on the work of the courts and the penal system was only just beginning.

5 Summary and Conclusions

In the course of this research into the effectiveness of the FSS, scientists and police officers responsible for different aspects of a large sample of cases were interviewed to assess the nature of their relationship and to build up as comprehensive a picture as possible of the outcome of their joint efforts. Developments at court were examined, but only indirectly (neither observation of trials nor any interviews with legal personnel were attempted). The main findings were as follows:

*The police refer a small—and, recently, under pressure from the FFS, a diminishing—proportion of cases for forensic analysis, which tends to be tried only when other avenues have already been well explored.

*Cases where the FSS is approached tend to be of above-average seriousness, while different police forces vary quite considerably in the extent to which they make use of the FSS.

*The FSS provided useful assistance to the police in over two-thirds of cases studied.

*The FSS is generally used to confirm the case against suspects who have already been identified; they may well have been charged before the FSS is contacted by the police.

*Where the police wanted to confirm existing evidence, the forensic report provided the required result in 60 per cent of cases.

*In an important minority—7 per cent—of cases with a suspect, the suspect was fully absolved by the forensic report.

*Forces making frequent use of the FSS found the service to be helpful just as often as did others. There was no sign that in their referral strategies the high-use forces had reached a point of diminishing returns. Indeed, slightly more of their cases were successfully cleared up than those from the low-use forces.

*Inadequate communications—in both directions—between the police and the FSS impede the two organisations from working together with maximum effectiveness. The FSS sometimes finds itself operating on the basis of insufficient information from the police, who themselves are not always fully informed about the needs and capabilities of the FSS, or the danger of contamination. A further problem of communication is that forensic reports do not have quite so strong an impact as they might.

A question of resources

In 1984, when the cost of FSS salaries and associated expenditure was a little over £7 million in England and Wales excluding London, the FSS estimated that the cost per case—leaving aside the less expensive categories of blood-alcohol and drugs analysis—was about £300. Some allowance should be made for the cost of Scenes of Crimes Officers, as a proportion of their time is devoted to the collection of evidence for FSS analysis. (The greater part of SOCO effort is spent on fingerprint work.) Including an arbitrary 20 per cent of SOCO costs, therefore, the figure rises to around £400. On the basis that seven out of ten cases provided useful assistance to the police, and writing off those which did not, the cost of each successful case was therefore £425 (or £550, including SOCO costs).

Comparison with other investigative strategies is very difficult. The crimes solved by different means have different characteristics and vary in gravity; nor are methods of solving crimes often interchangeable. For what it is worth, however, the cost of each case successfully handled by the fingerprint service was nearly £900. (This figure includes the full costs of SOCOs, and is based on a cost of £39 million for staff and running costs to solve nearly 50,000 cases in the UK.) The cost of clearing up cases by the CID, without recourse to either form of technical support, was over £550 on the basis of staff costs alone (in 1984 there were nearly 17,000 detectives in England and Wales), providing one excludes self-detecting offences such as shoplifting, and those which would not have been solved if they had not been 'taken into consideration'; if allowance were made for CID running costs, and for the input by uniformed branch, that figure would undoubtedly increase substantially.

On the basis of these contrasting figures, the cost of referrals to the FSS is far from excessive. Certainly it is not out of line with the cost of investigating crimes by other means, although the cost of consulting the FSS would need to be added on to the cost of investigation by the CID (the same point would also apply, at least to some extent, to the cost of fingerprint service involvement). In practice, of course, the police generally have only limited leeway in deciding which technical services to employ. Services such as the FSS or fingerprints or the police national computer are, fundamentally, complementary rather than conflicting. If one excludes murders and perhaps other exceptionally serious offences, use of the FSS is to some extent a matter of last resort, so far as the types of case covered by this research are concerned.

The key resource issue for the FSS is whether forces are referring cases at the "right" rate. This study suggests that forces which make relatively heavy

use of the FSS have not yet reached a point of diminishing retu
high-use forces actually had a slightly higher clear-up rate for the
they submitted than low-use forces, and derived additional benei
The study leaves open the possibility, therefore, that low-use fo
improve their detection rates by referring more cases to the FSS
does not do is show whether this would be the best way of u
additional resources. Would the costs incurred in increasing referral rates be
justified in terms of the resultant extra detections? Would the savings made
by reducing referral rates offset the lost opportunities for detection? These
are, unfortunately, much easier questions to ask than answer; they imply
knowledge of the marginal costs of improving detection rates both through
forensic analysis and through its alternatives, and this knowledge is simply
not available.

The cost of increased referrals by low-use forces could perhaps be absorbed
by a general sharpening-up of referral strategies on the part of all police
forces, if this were carried out in close co-operation with the FSS. This
report has shown that the outcome of the work of the FSS varies by
offence categories (see chapter 3, especially table 5). The proportion of cases
strengthened varied between 17 and 73 per cent for different offence categories
(or between 25 and 71 per cent if cases without suspects are excluded). That
is a substantial discrepancy, and one which emphasises the need for the
police and FSS to think more carefully about the reasons for submitting
cases for forensic analysis. It would however be foolish simply to suggest
that fewer cases from the unproductive categories should be examined: the
relative seriousness of the different kinds of offence also needs to be taken
into account. The effect of forensic work on sexual cases is relatively
disappointing compared with that concerned with thefts, but, to the officer
investigating a sexual offence, it may still be right to turn to the FSS even if the
likelihood of gaining useful information is comparatively poor. Nevertheless,
efforts to upgrade the quality of referrals might usefully be concentrated
especially on those offence categories where, at the moment, the results of
forensic analysis tend to be negative (sexual cases, damage, robberies). While
research can point to broad areas of concern, detailed action is best planned
jointly by police and FSS, at the level of force/laboratory.

An improvement in communications between police and FSS might help the
police to derive greater benefit from the submission of all types of cases.
For instance, had the widespread scepticism to be found among the police
about the usefulness of the documents section been properly appreciated
within the FSS, greater efforts would undoubtedly have been made to get to
the heart of this problem, and to educate the police as to the circumstances
where a referral to the handwriting specialists is likely to be worthwhile. If
some or all of the various suggestions outlined in the remainder of this
chapter for fostering closer co-operation between the FSS and the police
were found to be practicable and were implemented, they too would help to

boost the productivity of the FSS. These recommendations, taken as a package, do not imply any additional expenditure, but should themselves result in at least modest savings. It is however necessary to add that the resources of the FSS—above all, its staff—are already under considerable pressure, and that any leeway for carrying through changes is probably fairly tight. Training and communications are among the areas hard hit by resource constraints experienced by the FSS in recent years.

Communications between the FSS and the police

Communications between the FSS and the police need to be improved both so as to ensure that referrals—the input to the FSS—are as good as they can be and also to maximise the impact of forensic reports, or the output of the FSS. There are a number of ways in which, at every stage of the forensic process, better communications might help to upgrade both input and output. However, before making any suggestions for closer links between police and FSS, it is vital to emphasise that the FSS needs to be visibly independent of the police, if it is to be respected by the courts and by the public. Members of the FSS have to be able to get on the right wavelength with the police and also to maintain the necessary detachment for them to present their reports—and their expert evidence in court—with complete honesty and integrity, irrespective of the extent to which it may help the prosecution or the defence. And so, paradoxical as it may at first seem, there is a clear need for the FSS to reduce its isolation from the defence side. This is a matter to which attention will be drawn occasionally in the course of this section—which lists a number of proposals designed to improve the quality both of referrals and reports, on the basis of improved communications between FSS and police— and especially at the end.

1. There is a need to do more to ensure that all police officers—both detectives and uniformed officers—are suitably competent to deal with physical aspects of scenes of crime. While only detectives require in-depth knowledge, uniformed officers should be aware of basic procedures for routine handling of physical evidence, and they should also be able to safeguard, temporarily, the scene of any more serious crime at which they might be the first to arrive. This report has shown that evidence is sometimes mishandled—with potentially serious consequences by way of contamination—and that this is due to a lack of awareness that could and should be remedied by some basic training. Such training need not be extensive, but it should be practical in its emphasis.

2. The supply and availability of proper packaging facilities should be reappraised, to make sure these are adequate. This too would help to reduce the danger of contamination.

3. Improved training for detectives might usefully be integrated with the provision of better management information for the CID, which in turn

implies a need for joint monitoring of cases by police and FSS. (See below). The sharpening of referral skills is something which all detectives need to undertake from time to time, both to brush up on established techniques of forensic analysis and to keep abreast of new ones. Currently, despite having attended various training courses, officers tend to learn individually—almost by trial and error—what methods are actually useful, and are not always aware of the capabilities of the FSS. More needs to be done by way of on-the-job guidance as well as training. Conceivably, the use of designated liaison officers of a junior rank within police forces, at divisional or sub-divisional level, might also help.

4. The HOLAB form which investigating officers submit to the laboratory (along with the items of evidence) needs both to be redesigned and to be completed more thoroughly than is sometimes the case at present. If the scientist is to do his job effectively, he needs to have as complete an assessment as possible both of the incident and of the needs of the police. Officers should be encouraged to provide detailed information, especially in serious or complicated cases, and to indicate in full the continuity of all evidence from the time of its initial discovery onwards. If appropriate, witness statements and photographs should be appended to the HOLAB by the investigating officer: these too can help the scientist.

5. The effectiveness of referrals needs to be reviewed regularly and systematically by the FSS and the police. It would not be sensible for all cases to be scrutinised continually, but some or all of those from one of the half-dozen forces using each laboratory might conceivably be examined each year, perhaps jointly by police and FSS. In this way every force would gain information about its referrals at least once or twice a decade, while the FSS—which currently receives virtually no feedback on any regular basis for the vast majority of cases—would be able to monitor its work in a selective but thorough way.

6. The FSS should place more emphasis on promoting good communications with the police. An element of reorganisation is called for at each laboratory, to provide a more approachable advice service to police officers, to reach out to police forces (in disseminating information and helping with training), and so as to scrutinise incoming and outgoing cases. One way in which all this might be done would be to replace existing police liaison sections with information and reception units, staffed by a mixture of scientists and other professionals, rather than—as at present—by a slightly autonomous group of police officers (with only minimal clerical support), who spend much of their stint at the laboratory getting to know the place and its ways, and then still find themselves merely passing on queries to scientists, or acting as highly paid receptionists. An information and reception unit of the kind suggested could still include at least one serving or retired police officer. At present, as this report has shown, the police liaison staff are often by-passed when investigating officers and

43

scientists get in touch with each other, which lends extra emphasis to the need for a review of this area. A placement of a year or two in a unit of the kind proposed could be seen as a natural stage in the career development of those scientists likely to assume positions of managerial responsibility, while the unit might conceivably be headed by the deputy director of the laboratory.

7. Occasional short-term attachments of police officers to the FSS and vice versa would, in principle, do more to help members of both organisations to understand each other's requirements and point of view than the present selective arrangements whereby a few officers monopolise a limited number of posts at FSS laboratories for two to three years, while very few scientists ever visit police forces at all. While such interchanges are awkward to arrange, which would limit their numbers, there are several stages in their careers when some detectives and scientists would benefit from the chance to spend varying periods of time on attachment to each other's organisations.

8. The FSS ought to review its approach to report-writing quite fundamentally. The most important requirement after scientific accuracy is that all reports should make full sense to the layman. At present this is not always the case, which weakens the impact of the scientists' work. In general, the reports need to be as comprehensive as possible. If, for instance, the scientist does not examine every single item, he should say why he did not do so, rather than leave the reader to draw possibly erroneous conclusions. The FSS tends to deal in approximations to certainty, and it needs to consider, with other interested parties, how it can best express—as precisely as possible—the likelihood of a particular finding implying a wider conclusion. It might be helpful if the relevant HOLAB form, or appropriate sections of it, were to be appended to the scientist's report, and referred to if necessary; as it is, the information contained in the HOLAB crucially underpins the scientist's own report, but it does so in a way that is implicit, or hidden. If a change of this kind were to be made, it would enable the scientist to refer more explicitly to the wider circumstances of the case. It would also be useful if reports were to be word-processed. This would make it simpler to check that they were intelligible—as well as being scientifically accurate—and to revise them as often as necessary, with the minimum of difficulty.

9. The problem of delays needs fresh thought. An information and reception unit of the kind mentioned might help in planning the work of the laboratory, and in liaising effectively between investigating officers and scientists over the time taken to examine and report on cases. Here too a technological input might bring dividends: if cases were logged not in a cumbersome ledger but on a micro-computer—and up-to-date information added as necessary—FSS management would be better placed than it is at present to keep track of cases, to allocate manpower, and to try to meet

any police or court deadlines, or at least keep officers informed. The problem of delay is partly a question of resources, but it is also a matter of managing those actually available as effectively as possible, in close partnership with the police.

This list of ways in which the FSS and the police might work together more effectively is far from exhaustive, but it is one which it is hoped will help in improving both the input to the FSS and, most crucially of all, its output. Forensic analysis already contributes significantly to the work of the police, but there is still some additional potential which could be realised.

It is also vital that, if the FSS reduces its isolation from the police, it should likewise open up on the defence side, in the interests of evenhandedness. The suggestion has already been made that at least part of the HOLAB form should be appended to the scientist's report: this would enable the defence to have a clearer picture of any assumptions about the offence underlying the scientist's report. If a reception and information unit of the kind suggested were to be introduced, that too would make it easier for the FSS to be contacted by the defendant's legal representative. Scientists not infrequently find themselves discussing cases or explaining their conclusions on the telephone to police investigating officers, when they hardly ever talk to the defence side. Yet, were scientists more readily approachable by both sides in a case, this might ultimately enhance the impact of forensic reports. Furthermore, the readiness of the FSS to examine items at the request of the defence needs fresh consideration and a new emphasis. Finally, not least as a sign that it is addressing itself to such issues, the FSS might publish an annual or biennial report, which should be as informative as possible about the important public service it undoubtedly is.

APPENDICES

Appendix A: Survey design and methods

The approach adopted

The initial sample was drawn at the two laboratories by taking a consecutive series of roughly 150 cases for each police force. The sequence of cases chosen was virtually predefined by the need to include those which had completed their progress through the courts, but which were no older than necessary. The overall sample covered slightly different periods for the four forces, because each of them referred varying numbers of cases per month. The Derbyshire cases comprised those submitted to the Birmingham laboratory between January 1984 and February 1985; the West Midlands batch was simply the two months of May and June 1984; the Bedfordshire cases, as submitted to the Huntingdon laboratory, covered March 1984 to December 1984; and the Essex ones, July 1984 to December 1984. The pattern of cases in the research sample compared reasonably closely with that of the national caseload of the FSS, as is shown by table 1.

Table 1
Research sample and relevant components of FSS caseload for 1984

Category	Research sample		FSS caseload	
	Number of cases	*Per cent*	*Number of cases*	*Per cent*
Homicide	25	4	422	4
Woundings	62	11	1,147	10
Sexual	84	14	1,508	13
Burglary	133	22	3,030	26
Robbery	16	3	343	3
Theft	97	16	1,673	14
Arson	94	16	1,370	12
Damage	60	10	1,332	11
Coinage	1	<1	17	<1
Explosives	8	1	150	1
Safes	1	<1	10	<1
Unclassified	12	2	816	7
Total	593	100	11,818	100

The overall size of the sample was 593, with a range of between 143 and 157 cases for each of the four different forces. A data collection form was completed for every single case, by a member of the research team. In 547 out of the 593 cases (92 per cent) the scientist acting as reporting officer completed the appropriate questionnaire (the rate of completion was slightly lower for cases submitted to the Birmingham laboratory than for the Huntingdon one, because of the longer time-lag for part of the Derbyshire component of the sample, coupled with staff turnover at Birmingham). The two-thirds subsample of hoped-for police interviews (395) yielded 330 which were actually completed: an 84 per cent success rate, spread fairly evenly between each of the four forces, and equivalent to well over half the total sample. Some of the 593 cases had—in addition to the data collection form—both scientist and police questionnaires; others had only one of these, or neither. Key details of the completion rates for the three forms are presented in table 2 which, reading across from left to right, shows a fairly even shrinkage from the original sample.

Table 2
Rates of completion for the data collection form, the scientist questionnaire and the police questionnaire, by police force.

	Completed data collection forms		Completed scientist questionnaires		Completed police questionnaires	
	No.	%	No.	%	No.	%
Bedfordshire (Huntingdon)	148	25	142	24	81	14
Essex (Huntingdon)	145	24	143	24	83	14
West Midlands (Birmingham)	157	26	140	24	85	14
Derbyshire (Birmingham)	143	24	122	21	81	14
Total	593	100	547	92	330	56

Note
1. Percentages are all a function of the overall total of 593 cases.

Discarded research strategies

It is worth explaining what was left undone, and why. First, no effort was made to conduct any kind of organisational experiment involving, say, increased or reduced use of the FSS by one or more police forces, matched against another force or forces acting as controls. No attempt was made even to compare a sample of crimes where the police sought the help of the FSS with a similar group of offences where no such referral was made.

These research strategies were ruled out because, although potentially highly fruitful, they would have been enormously demanding of resources and, in the case of any experiment, would have been disruptive for the police and the FSS. Even the matching of FSS cases against crimes not submitted to the FSS would have been difficult to organise properly, and would have needed a much greater research investment: Peterson, Mihajlovic and Gilliland (1983), who adopted this course in the United States, took over three years to carry out their project, and were backed up by a strong support team.

Opting only for a retrospective descriptive study, it still seemed difficult to track cases through the courts (other than by interviewing the police officers involved, as was done). Although it might have been attractive to ask judges and magistrates, or prosecution and defence, for their views of the FSS evidence (juries are barred to researchers, by statute), logistical difficulties and resource constraints made it impossible to do this. Observational study of the impact of FSS testimony in court would likewise have been difficult to arrange, especially for a sizeable sample. So the idea of carrying out any separate study of the courts was abandoned.

Appendix B: Text of three reports by scientists

1. Case involving glass transfer at the scene of a burglary

"On 1 April 1985 the following items were received in the laboratory from Shire Police:

(1) ABC/1 Pair of socks—Rear of Doctor's Surgery, County Town.
(2) XYZ/1 Glass sample—Window, Doctor's Surgery, County Town.

Nine glass fragments, all having freshly broken appearance, have been recovered from the socks (1). Two of these glass fragments have a flat original surface which agrees in microscopial appearance with the glass sample (2). The refractive indices of these two glass fragments and a further three glass fragments recovered from the socks (1) have been measured and agree with the refractive index of the glass sample (2). One of the glass fragments with an original surface recovered from the socks (1) has been further examined and found to have an elemental composition which agrees with that of the glass sample (2).

In my opinion, the glass recovered from the socks could well have come from the window of the Doctor's Surgery in County Town."

[This case fell outside the research sample.]

2. Case involving blood shed at the scene of a burglary

"On 1 August 1984 the following items were received at the laboratory from the Shire Police:
1 (JR 2) Sample of stain from floor ⎤
2 (JR 3) Sample of stain from floor ⎮ Sports Club
3 (JR 4) Sample of stain from floor ⎮ County Town
4 (JR 5) Sample of stain from floor ⎦
5 (CD/1) Blood sample—Bill SIKES

The blood sample (5—B SIKES) belongs to groups EAP BA, Hp 2.

Item (2) consists of flakes of dried blood. Some of this blood has been tested and found to be of human origin and to belong to the same groups as the blood sample (5—B SIKES) namely EAP BA, Hp 2.

53

The blood (2) from the floor of the Sports Club, therefore, could have come from B SIKES.

Approximately 1 in 6 of the population of Great Britain belong to the groups EAP BA, Hp 2.

Chemical reactions indicating the presence of traces of blood have been obtained from items (1, 3 and 4). Grouping tests performed on item (4) have been unsuccessful. Items (1 and 3) have not been tested further.''

[The scientist assessed his contribution in this case as crucial; the investigating officer felt it was only minimal, and had produced insufficient evidence to sustain a charge, despite the existence of other evidence of a circumstantial nature.]

3. Case involving footprints found at the scene of a burglary

"On 1 July 1984 the following items were received from the Shire Police:

1 (QP/1) Pair of shoes—John SMITH
2 (QP/2) Pair of shoes—Clive KELLY
3 (AR/1) Cast of shoeprints ⎫
4 (AR/2) Cast of shoeprints ⎭ Rear Garden, 22 Short Street

The pair of baseball shoes (1) are approximately size 9 and made by 'Hi-Tec'. The shoes (1) are in a fair condition although clearly show signs of wear. The undersurface pattern consists of zig-zag bars with circular features on the ball of the sole and on the heel.

The pair of training shoes (2) are of size 7 and made by 'Botra'. The shoes (2) are in a generally worn condition. The undersurface pattern consists of short straight bars. Most of these bars are considerably worn and there are damage (cut) features in some of the bars.

The cast (3) shows two impressions made by footwear with the same two undersurface patterns as those of the two pairs of shoes (1) and (2). The major footwear impression has been made by a right shoe with the same undersurface pattern and mould (size) as the right shoe in (2). The cast shows that the bars of the shoe responsible are worn in the same way as the undersurfaces of the right shoe in (2). Furthermore a significant damage feature in the leading edge of one of the bars agrees exactly in shape and position with a feature in the footwear impression in the cast (3). The other footwear impression is only partial but shows the circular feature on the ball of the sole of the shoes in (1). There is insufficient detail in this second impression to associate it specifically with a particular shoe with this type of undersurface pattern.

The cast (4) shows a footwear impression made by a left shoe with the same undersurface pattern and mould (size) as that of the left shoe in (1). There is insufficient detail in this impression to associate it specifically with the left shoe in (1).

Both pairs of shoes (1) and (2) had deposits of dried mud on the undersurface. These deposits have not been compared with dried mud adhering to the casts (3) and (4).

Conclusion

The right shoe (2) from Clive KELLY has made one of the footwear impressions shown in the cast (3) from 22 Short Street.

The Shoes (1) from John SMITH could have made footwear impressions shown in the casts (3) and (4) from 22 Short Street."

[The scientist assessed his contribution in this case as crucial; the investigating officer was uncertain as to the value of the forensic analysis—he felt the evidence was "not strong enough to run in court."]

Appendix C: The case of 'the Fox' and its consequences

The first part of this appendix, an account of the hunt for 'the Fox', has been written from the point of view of the FSS, by staff at the Huntingdon laboratory. The case is a good example of how the FSS can help the police to carry out a major investigation. The second part of this appendix, which is concerned with the impact of 'the Fox' on the wider pattern of police referrals to Huntingdon, has been written by the main author of the report.

The case of 'the Fox': the role of the FSS

Malcolm Fairley, or 'the Fox' as he was called by the press, committed a series of more than 80 offences after moving into the Bedfordshire area. The crimes were carried out in places served by five different police forces. All were burglaries, many of which involved only minor thefts, while on other occasions there were serious, premeditated sexual assaults. Key offences are shown in the following list, incorporating dates and locations:

11 April 1984	Indecent assault on elderly woman, Bedfordshire.
10 May 1984	Homosexual assault and theft of shotgun, Thames Valley.
6 June 1984	Theft of shotgun, Hertfordshire.
9 June 1984	Two offences in the course of the same night, both in Bedfordshire. One was a burglary and the other an attempted rape, during which the victim's husband was shot and injured. The two offences were linked by an anorak stolen in the course of the first one, and left at the scene of the second.
6 July 1984	Indecent assault of woman, Bedfordshire.
10 July 1984	Rape of woman, Bedfordshire.
12 July 1984	Rape of young woman, Thames Valley.
17 August 1984	Two offences on the same day: rape of a woman in Yorkshire, and an assault on a woman in County Durham.
9 September 1984	Stabbing, Thames Valley.

The assaults all occurred in the early hours of the morning, and had other factors in common such as the wearing of a mask and the carrying of a firearm. Following the northern offences committed on 17 August, 'the Fox' buried the gun—and left other items—in a copse by the M18 where he had temporarily hidden his car.

Initial laboratory work

Items from the offences committed in April and May were examined at the Huntingdon and Aldermaston laboratories respectively. Nothing useful was found. The firearms department at Huntingdon identified the type of cartridge used from wads recovered following the shooting incident (9 June), but was not able to discover anything of value about the weapon. Work on the rape of 10 July was still in progress at the Huntingdon laboratory when items from the rape of 12 July were submitted. It was only at this stage that the FSS became fully aware that a series was involved. On 16 July the head of the biology department at Huntingdon was attached on a full-time basis to the incident room set up by the police at Dunstable, and it was agreed that all forensic work on cases in the series would be concentrated at Huntingdon.

The attachment

The scientist attached to the police incident room had a number of objectives:

*To enable the police to make the most effective use of the facilities at Huntingdon.

*To liaise with the rest of the FSS (and the Metropolitan Police Forensic Science Laboratory) about other sexual offences, and assess the likelihood of the same offender being involved.

*To attend relevant management meetings, and advise the officer with overall responsibility for the investigation (Detective Chief Superintendent, Bedfordshire).

*To read all statements and—through participation in the daily briefing of the investigation team, or in any other way—to suggest possible lines of enquiry.

The scientist wrote frequent brief informal reports to the officer in charge of the case—some 40 pages of typescript in all. He worked long hours, usually attending the incident room from about 9.00 am to about 10.00 pm. In retrospect, this was unrealistic. Ideally, two scientists ought to have been attached, particularly to devote adequate time to theorising about the nature of 'the Fox'. The handling of large amounts of information in a major police investigation is the kind of research problem where scientists can be of considerable help.

Detailed laboratory work

Staff at Huntingdon addressed themselves initially to the following questions:

*Which crimes belonged to the series? (This line of enquiry was also aimed at pinpointing patterns of behaviour.)

*What kinds of clothes did 'the Fox' wear?

*What range of tools did he own? (Various implements were used to break into premises.)

*What was his occupation?

Scene-of-crime visits established at an early stage that there were common shoe-sole patterns at the premises where the first two rapes occurred. The laboratory was able to identify the type of shoes, and provided the incident room with a pair. Several of the offences were linked by tool marks, which also indicated the range of tools in the possession of 'the Fox'.

The scientist in charge of the biological aspects managed to determine the probable blood groups of 'the Fox', and was able to assemble considerable information about clothing fabrics and the gloves worn by 'the Fox'. The textile work was difficult and time-consuming: the FSS is normally only concerned as to whether fibres match a control sample from a known garment. However, enough was discovered to enable the scientist at the police incident room to ask for a search of its computerised data collection for sightings of men in particular clothes.

In August, a scientist from the chemistry department visited the copse in Yorkshire where the police had recovered the gun (stolen on 6 June) and a hood which had been made from a piece of trouser leg. The chemist was able to establish not only that a car had been hidden there, but also its exact colour, approximate size and shape, and possible make. It was this information which led the two detectives making a routine screening interview of one of several hundred suspects to believe—correctly—that the man they were talking to was 'the Fox'.

The arrest took place on 11 September 1984. On the following day, the FSS confirmed that Fairley had the right blood groups for 'the Fox', and that a tool belonging to him had definitely been used in one of the burglaries. The police established that a partial palm print, found on the bag in which the gun had been buried, had been made by Fairley. Soon afterwards, the FSS confirmed that Fairley's car was, almost beyond doubt, the one which had been hidden in the copse in Yorkshire.

The magnitude of the FSS involvement

More than 800 items were submitted. Some 600 were examined. Two reporting officers were almost continually engaged in the work for three months. One other scientist did nothing else for six months. For a period of about a week, after items had been recovered from the copse, virtually the entire staff of the chemistry and biology departments at Huntingdon were devoted to the work. All six Home Office laboratories provided information that was helpful, as did the Metropolitan Police Forensic Science Laboratory. All but one of the Home Office laboratories—and the MPFSL—undertook additional benchwork.

The Huntingdon laboratory co-ordinated the statements—those from three departments at Huntingdon together with others from Aldermaston, Chorley and Wetherby—into a single, indexed package, of 80 pages.

The impact of 'the Fox' on referrals

The chase for 'the Fox' (June to September 1984) had such a massive impact on the whole range of activity of Bedfordshire Police—including the investigation of other cases where physical evidence was sent to Huntingdon—that this in turn had an adverse effect on results from the laboratory.

Officers in Essex were not troubled by 'the Fox'; nor was there any change in their assessment of the contribution made to cases by the FSS as between the period when 'the Fox' was being hunted and the remaining three months of the year (the Essex cases covered the six months from July to December). The consistency over time of the ratings given by Essex Police also suggests that the quality of work done at the laboratory was not affected by the scientists having to cope with the 800 exhibits associated with 'the Fox' (and while staff at Huntingdon did vary the amount of time devoted to cases, they did not, in the process, discriminate between the two forces). The ratings given by the Bedfordshire Police did however dip very sharply for cases sent to the laboratory while the hunt for 'the Fox' was in progress: thereafter, they largely reverted to their former level (the Bedfordshire cases covered the ten months from March to December). This is illustrated in table 1.

If one excludes the 27 Bedfordshire cases for June through to September, and compares the remaining Bedfordshire cases—together with those from Essex—against the cases submitted to the Birmingham laboratory, the respective sets of ratings are, as is shown by table 2 (columns two and three), fairly comparable.

Before ending this appendix, it is worth looking at the underlying reasons for the deterioration in the results for Bedfordshire cases submitted during the hunt for 'the Fox', not least because of what they show about the differences between successful and unsuccessful referrals. There were indeed changes in the percentages of cases in the various offence categories. However, these partially cancelled each other out. Of the two major productive categories—violence and burglaries—only the former showed a proportional decrease while 'the Fox' was at large. Of the important but less productive

Table 1
Police officers' assessment of the contribution made by FSS Huntingdon to their investigations

Officers' ratings	Bedfordshire			Essex	
	Pre-Fox (Mar-May)	Fox-time (Jun-Sep)	After Fox (Oct-Dec)	Fox-time (July-Sep)	After Fox (Oct-Dec)
	%	%	%	%	%
Rating of crucial or substantial or useful	65	34	53	43	44
Minimal, little or no help or uncertain	36	67	48	57	57
	100	100	100	100	100
n =	31	27	23	37	46

Table 2
Police officers' ratings of cases handled by the laboratories at Birmingham and Huntingdon

Officers' ratings	All cases sent to Huntingdon	Cases sent to Huntingdon except the 27 Bedfordshire ones when 'the Fox' at large	All cases sent to Birmingham	All cases sent to both labs
	%	%	%	%
Crucial substantial or useful	47	50	52	49
Minimal, little or no help; or uncertain	53	50	48	51
	100	100	100	100
n =	164	137	166	330

categories—sexual cases and damage—only the second of these increased in proportion. Looking instead at the percentage of cases in which a suspect had been identified, there was a more clear-cut contrast: there was a known suspect in only 63 per cent of Bedfordshire cases while 'the Fox' was at large, as opposed to 82 per cent of all other Bedfordshire cases. This further emphasises the importance of the police knowing 'who dunnit' in helping to shape the outcome of FSS involvment.

Appendix D: Police Officers' and scientists' ratings of the work of the FSS

This table illustrates the extent to which police officers' ratings of the contribution of the FSS to investigations matched those of scientists. The figures given in brackets are percentages.

	Police officers' ratings					
Scientists' ratings	Crucial/ substantial	Useful	Minimal/ little	None	Don't know	Row totals
Crucial/ substantial	51 (58)	20 (34)	8 (22)	12 (16)	12 (27)	103 (34)
Useful	21 (24)	24 (41)	7 (19)	7 (9)	2 (5)	61 (20)
Minimal/little	8 (9)	10 (17)	12 (32)	26 (35)	5 (11)	61 (20)
None	6 (7)	2 (3)	4 (11)	23 (31)	2 (5)	37 (12)
Don't know	2 (2)	3 (5)	6 (16)	7 (9)	23 (52)	41 (14)
Total N Column %	88 (100)	59 (100)	37 (100)	75 (100)	44 (100)	303 (100)

Correlation = 0.49

Appendix E: Questionnaires

Project serial number .... [/   /   ]
                        (1) (2) (3)

Booklet number .... [   ]
              (4)

Lab: Bham (1) or Hunt (2) ...... [   ]
              (5)

Card number .... [/   ]
              (6) (7)

DATA COLLECTION FORM FOR LABS

FSS crime category [01-20, ie 2 digits] .... [/   ]
FSS reference number ....

A. Section to be completed from HOLAB 3 and FSS file

Basic details

1. Police reference number [vict.if DK]: ....

2. Police force. Circle number:

Derbyshire	1
West Midlands	2
Bedfordshire	3
Essex	4
Other	5

3. HO crime category (main) [01-99–2 digits] .... [/   ]

Additionally, give a brief description of the characteristics of the incident

....

....

....

....

[Continue elsewhere if necessary]

65

4. Place where incident occurred: ....

5. If subsidiary crime categories involved, what were their HO numbers?

[Enter 00 as defaults] .... [/] [/]

6. Name of main scientist—reporting officer [not in HOLAB 3]

....

7. Name of lead division. Circle number:

Biology	1
Chemistry	2
Toxicology/drugs	3
Documents	4
Firearms	5

8. Were other divisions also involved? Circle number:

Yes	1
No	2

9. If *yes* to previous question, which division(s)? Circle ALL relevant numbers:

Biology	1
Chemistry	2
Toxicology/drugs	3
Documents	4
Firearms	5
NR—no others involved	6

10. Name of police officer (ic investigation) ....

11. Phone of police officer ....

12. Address of police officer ....

13. Was a specific suspect(s) identified (by 1st HOLAB 3 date)? Circle number:

Yes	1
No	2
DK	3

14. If *yes* to previous question, name main (first) suspect ....

15. If *yes* to last-but-one question (13), were further known suspects also involved, as accomplices or as alternative suspects? Circle number:

Yes	1
No	2
DK	3
NR	4

16. If *yes* to previous question (15), note number and nature of other suspects

....

....

....

[Continue elsewhere if necessary]

17. Is there any reason to believe that main suspect was under suspicion/ investigation for other offences, or that this was a possible "series" offence? Circle number:

Yes 1
No 2
DK 3

18. Was (were) there one (or more) personal/individual victims (loss or hurt cases, actual or attempted)? Circle number:

Yes 1
No 2
DK 3

19. Was there a known corporate victim, eg a shop/company (actual or attempted cases)? Circle number:

Yes 1
No 2
DK 3

Offence details

20. Date of incident (6 digits; 3 pairs) .... [/ /]

Date of HOLAB 3 (6 digits; 3 pairs) .... [/ /]

21. Nature of (major) location. Circle number:

Residential indoors/involving building 1
Place of entertainment, indoors/involving building 2
Other, inside/involving building (specify: ....) 3
Out of doors, in street/public place 4
Out of doors, in private place (specify: ....) 5
Other, eg in vehicle (specify: ....) 6
DK 7

22. Degree of hurt to main victim. Circle FIRST applicable number:

Death	1
Sexual violation	2
Hospital overnight	3
Other physical hurt	4
No physical hurt	5
DK	6
No victim/NR	7

23. Extent of any monetary or other specified loss/damage. Circle number [will often be "DK"—is still important]:

£10,000 or over	1
£500 or over	2
£100 or over	3
Under £100	4
None/NR	5
DK	6

24. What contact was evident between main offender and victim/others? Circle number:

Substantial physical contact	1
Limited physical contact	2
None/NR	3
DK	4

Scene of crime and investigation details

25. Were there—as apparent anywhere in the whole file—any "contamination" problems relating *either* to the scene of the crime (and those victimised there) *or* to the handling/packaging of exhibits which subsequently affected *either* the scope of the scientific analysis *or* the way the scientist's conclusions were expressed? Circle number:

No such contamination problems with scene/victim or with handling/packaging 1
DK 2
Contamination problems with scene (or victim) 3
Contamination problems with handling/packaging 4
Contamination problems with scene/victim and with handling/packaging
.... 5

26. *If answers 3-5 selected* (ie contamination), describe circumstances:

....

....

....

[Continue elsewhere if necessary]

27. Whether (main/first) offender/suspect positively or tentatively identified by victim/witness. Circle FIRST appropriate number:

Offender/suspect identified by name 1
Offender/suspect id'd by own car no./other such detail 2
Description of offender/suspect provided in some detail 3
Only limited description of offender recalled 4
No description of offender available 5
DK 6

28. If *answers 1-4 selected*, was such identification provided only by victim(s) or did it also come from independent witnesses? [Independent witnesses include police witnesses unless in victim capacity.] Circle number:

Info from single victim only 1
Info from 2+ victims; no independent witnesses 2
Info only from one or more independent witnesses 3
Info both from victim(s) and also from ind. witness(es) 4
DK 5
NR 6

29. As apparant—how did the police investigation proceed (up to date of first HOLAB 3)? Circle ALL relevant numbers:

Suspect found at/near scene/gave self up 01
Suspect's ID known from an early stage 02
Victim's or other description acted upon 03
House to house enquiries 04
Suspect's ready access/obvious motive investigated 05
Search of property of possible suspects/accomplices 06
Observations/trap 07
Police knowledge/intelligence/use of informers 08
Fingerprint search 09
Photograph albums 10
Suspect implicated by accomplice 11
Other (specify ....) 12
None of above apparent 13

30. Summarise briefly the progress of the police investigation as apparent from the HOLAB 3 and any other associated docs. on the file:

....

....

....

....

[Continue elsewhere if necessary]

31. Did the police—at any point prior to the completion of the scientist's report—supply copies of witness statements or comparable documents to the lab? Circle answer:

$$\text{Yes} \dots\dots\dots\dots\dots\dots \quad 1$$

$$\text{No} \dots\dots\dots\dots\dots\dots \quad 2$$

32. If *yes* to previous question, describe nature of such documents:

....

....

....

33. Were there apparently any significant developments in the police investigation—which might in any way have affected the work which the FSS was asked to do—*after* the submission of the first HOLAB 3 but *before* the completion of the FSS report? Circle number:

$$\text{Yes, certainly} \dots\dots\dots\dots\dots \quad 1$$

$$\text{Yes, possibly} \dots\dots\dots\dots\dots \quad 2$$

$$\text{No} \dots\dots\dots\dots\dots\dots\dots \quad 3$$

$$\text{DK} \dots\dots\dots\dots\dots\dots\dots \quad 4$$

34. If the answer to the previous question was *yes, certainly* or *Yes, possibly* explain what happened:

....

....

....

[Continue elsewhere if necessary]

35. Whether suspect arrested/charged [or warned of summonsing] by (1st) HOLAB 3 submission date. Circle number:

$$\text{Yes} \dots\dots\dots\dots\dots\dots \quad 1$$

$$\text{No} \dots\dots\dots\dots\dots\dots \quad 2$$

$$\text{DK} \dots\dots\dots\dots\dots\dots \quad 3$$

36. By whom forensic evidence found. Circle ALL relevant numbers:

Detective(s) 1
Uniformed police 2
Police SOC officer(s) 3
Civilian SOC officer(s) 4
Forensic scientist(s) 5
Other (specify ....) 6
DK 7

37. Number of items submitted for forensic analysis, in total. State number—
2 digits [check with report]: .... [/]

38. Nature of items submitted for forensic analysis (total listing). Circle ALL
relevant numbers:

Biological-sexual eg semen/vaginal 01
Hair 02
Blood 03
Other biological eg saliva, faeces 04
Glass 05
Glove(s) 06
Clothing/cloth/fibres 07
Shoes/footwear 08
Documents/implements associated with documents 09
Drugs and associated paraphernalia 10
Arson/fire-related 11
Serial numbers (specify what from ....) 12
Motor vehicle related (or parts of vehicles) 13
Explosives and residues etc 14
Firearms and ammunition etc 15
"Weapons" other than firearms 16
Paint 17
Poison 18
Soils and minerals 19
Dust and other traces 20
Tracks and impressions (shoe, tyre) 21
Tools/toolmarks 22
Other (specify ....) 23

39. Were the various items submitted for forensic analysis all delivered in
one batch (or at least as itemised in a single HOLAB 3)? Circle number:

Yes 1
No 2
DK 3

40. If *no* to previous question, were the extra items produced through the initiative of the police or of scientist(s)? Circle number:

Police initiative 1
Scientist(s) initiative 2
Joint initiative by police + scientist(s) 3
DK 4
NR 5

41. What main function/type of work did the police request (as in 13a of the first HOLAB 3)? Circle number:

Linking or matching of different substances/items 1
Identification of particular substances/items 2
General trawling for clues 3
Other (specify) 4

42. Did the police appear to have a secondary function/type of work in mind? Circle number:

Linking or matching of different substances/items 1
Identification of different substances/items 2
General trawling for clues 3
Other (specify ....) 4
No apparent secondary function/type of work—ie NR 5

43. What main objective did the police have in mind (as in 13a of the first HOLAB 3)? Circle number:

To see if/how a crime was committed 1
To analyse items for future reference/intelligence 2
To identify a previously unidentified suspect(s) 3
To strengthen/validate a case against a suspect(s) 4
Other (specify ....) 5

44. Did the police appear to have in mind a secondary objective? Circle number:

To see if/how a crime was committed 1
To analyse items for future reference/intelligence 2
To identify a previously unidentified suspect(s) 3
To strengthen/validate a case against a suspect 4
Other (specify ....) 5
No apparent secondary objective—ie NR 6

Outcome of FSS work [Leave HOLAB 3 for rest of file]

45. What did the FSS report(s) show? Briefly summarise findings:

....

....

....

[Continue elsewhere if necessary]

46. How significant a contribution did the main function/type of work originally requested of the FSS by the police (see Question 41) actually make to the investigation? Circle number [see separate guidelines]:

A crucial contribution	1
A substantial contribution	2
A useful contribution	3
A minimal contribution	4
Little contribution	5
No contribution	6
DK	7

47. Was the (original) main police objective (ie to show if/how offence committed, to analyse items, to pinpoint unidentified suspect, to strengthen/ validate a case etc, as in Question 43) actually achieved? Circle number:

In whole	1
In part	2
To a limited extent	3
Not at all	4
DK	5

48. Was a previously unsuspected/uncharged individual implicated (to any extent) by the scientific findings? Circle number:

Yes	1
No	2
DK	3

49. Was a previously suspected/charged person cleared (even if merely by default) by the scientific findings? Circle number:

Yes	1
No	2
DK	3

50. Was the case against an already suspected/charged person strengthened or sustained by the scientific findings? Circle number:

Yes	1
No	2
DK	3

51. If answer was *yes* to any of the *previous three questions*, how conclusive were the scientific findings in pointing to culpability (or otherwise) of particular individual(s)? Circle number:

Conclusive or virtually so	1
Strongly indicative	2
Limited strength only	3
Inconclusive	4
DK	5
NR	6

52. If the functions/objectives originally stipulated by the police were subsequently modified for any reason, prior to the report being written (see Question 33), comment on whether or not these revised goals were attained.

....

....

....

[Continue elsewhere if necessary]

53. Which categories were involved in conclusive or strongly indicative findings? [See Questions 38/51.] Circle ALL relevant numbers:

Biological-sexual eg semen/vaginal	01
Hair	02
Blood	03
Other biological eg saliva, faeces	04
Glass	05
Glove(s)	06
Clothing/cloth/fibres	07
Shoes/footwear	08
Documents/implements associated with documents	09
Drugs and associated paraphernalia	10
Arson/fire-related	11
Serial numbers (specify what from ....)	12
Motor vehicle related (or parts of vehicles)	13
Explosives and residues etc	14
Firearms and ammunition etc	15
"Weapons" other than firearms	16
Paint	17
Poison	18
Soils and minerals	19
Dust and other traces	20
Tracks and impressions (shoe, tyre)	21
Tools/toolmarks	22
Other (specify ....)	23

54. Were *any of the categories* of evidence *not* examined in full? Circle number:

One category not examined in full 1
Two categories not examined in full 2
Three categories not examined in full 3
Four (or more) categories not examined in full 4
DK 5
Every category examined in full 6

55. Total number of items *not* examined in full—compare HOLAB 3/report [2 digits] .... [/   ]

FSS reference number ....

Scientist's name ....

....

Project serial number .... [/   /   ]
                        (1) (2) (3)

Booklet number .... [   ]
                        (4)

Lab: Bham (1) or Hunt (2) ...... [   ]
                        (5)

Card number .... [/   ]
                        (6) (7)

....

B. Questionnaire—for reporting officer scientists

1. Did you visit the scene of the crime? Circle number:

Yes 1
No 2

2. If you visited the scene of the crime, do you think your visit was useful? Circle number:

Yes 1
No 2
Don't know 3
Not relevant—didn't visit scene ... 4

3. If you visited the scene, and found this visit useful, explain why [in relation to effectiveness, efficiency]

....
....
....
....
....

[Continue elsewhere if necessary]

4. Before you wrote your report, were you (or other scientists) ever in touch with the police officers handling the investigation—in any of the following four forms of contact/information exchange? Circle the appropriate number *for each of these four forms of contact*:

    i. Phone, personal

        Yes 1
        No 2
        DK 3

   ii. Phone, via liaison staff

        Yes 1
        No 2
        Don't know 3

  iii. Letter/written/telex

        Yes 1
        No 2
        Don't know 3

  iv. Face to face

        Yes 1
        No 2
        Don't know 3

5. Did the police—without additional prompting on your part—pass on sufficient information about the case (to facilitate efficient/effective handling)? Circle number:

        Yes 1
        No 2
        Don't know 3

6. If *no* to previous question (5), did you press the police for further details? Circle number:

Yes 1
No 2
Don't know 3
Not relevant—wasn't necessary ... 4

7. If *yes* to previous question (6), was that information forthcoming? Circle number:

Information forthcoming in full .. 1
Information forthcoming in part . 2
Information not forthcoming 3
Don't know 4
Not relevant—no information needed
.... 5

8. In section 13 of the HOLAB 3 the police specify "What is required to be established or proved in relation to the items submitted". How well would you say the job was specified? [Leaving aside the number of items submitted for examination.] Circle number:

Job was well specified 1
Job was tolerably specified 2
Job was poorly specified 3

9. If job was tolerably or poorly specified, give explanation:

....
....
....
....
[Continue elsewhere if necessary]

10. Did you—other than when giving evidence in open court—have any contact (whether written/phone/in person) with prosecutors/the prosecution side [ie not police]? Circle number:

Yes, before trial (including pre-trial reviews etc) 1
Yes, at trial stage 2
Yes, before trial and at trial stage 3
No 4
Don't know 5

11. Did you at any stage have any contact with non-FSS defence scientists? Circle number:

Yes 1
No 2
DK 3

12. Did you—other than when giving evidence in open court—have any contact (whether written/phone/in person) with legal representatives acting for the defence? Circle answer/number:

Yes, before trial (including pre-trial reviews etc) 1
Yes, at trial stage 2
Yes, before trial and at trial stage 3
No 4
Don't know 5

13. Did you give evidence in court? Circle number:

Yes 1
No 2
DK 3

14. In all, how many working days (or their equivalent) would you estimate that you devoted to this case (actual time, not elapsed time)? Circle number:

One day or a part of a day 1
Two to three days 2
Four to ten days 3
Over ten days 4
Don't know 5

15. In all, how many working days (or their equivalent) would you estimate that other FSS scientists (at every level, in aggregate) devoted to this case (actual time, not elapsed time)? Circle number:

One day or a part of a day 1
Two to three days 2
Four days to ten days 3
Over ten days 4
Don't know 5

16. Did the police ever explain the outcome of their investigation and/or how your work had contributed to this? Circle number:

Police gave explanation 1
Police did not give explanation ... 2
Explanation only gained in other way
.... 3
Don't know 4

17. Irrespective of feedback, how significant a contribution do you think your work made to the investigation of this case? Circle number [see separate guidelines]:

A crucial contribution 1
A substantial contribution 2
A useful contribution 3
A minimal contribution 4
Little contribution 5
No contribution 6
Don't know/uncertain 7

18. How many years spent in FSS? Circle number:

1–4 years 1
5–9 years 2
10–19 years 3
20+ years 4

19. In how many FSS establishments—including present one—has reporting officer worked? [NB For the purposes of this question only, count Nottingham and Huntingdon as one establishment.] Circle number:

One—ie present establishment only ...
.... 1
Two establishments 2
Three establishments 3
Four establishments (or more) 4

20. Qualification(s) obtained (at university or equivalent). Circle LAST APPLICABLE number:

First degree 1
One year (or upwards) of postgraduate study 2
PhD (or equivalent) 3

Project serial number .... [/ /]
(1) (2) (3)

Booklet number .... [ ]
(4)

Lab: Bham (1) or Hunt (2) ...... [ ]
(5)

Card number .... [/]
(6) (7)

79

STUDY OF FORENSIC SCIENCE SERVICE: QUESTIONNAIRE FOR POLICE

Preliminary details (check or complete as appropriate)

  i. Police force. [Circle appropriate number.]

Derbyshire	1
West Midlands	2
Bedfordshire	3
Essex	4
Other	5

  ii. Name/letter [not in brackets] of division: .... [/]

  iii. Police reference number [or vict.]: ....

  iv. Nature + location of incident .... + ...

  v. Date of FSS report (Essex, Derbyshire) .... [/ /]

Basic details about the offence and the investigation

1. Was the investigation concerned with a single incident, or was a specific series of linked offences apparently involved? [Circle appropriate number.]

Single incident only	1
Single incident, but possible links with other incidents	2
Specific series of linked offences	3
Other (specify ....)	4
Don't know	5

2. Was there a victim who was hurt (in the FSS-linked incident)? [Hurt = physical hurt of human victim.] [Circle appropriate number.]

No	1	SKIP TO Q.5
Don't know	2	SKIP TO Q.5
Yes	3	ASK Q.3

3. What degree of hurt did the (main/worst affected) victim suffer? [Circle the FIRST APPLICABLE number.]

Death	1
Sexual violation	2
Hospital overnight†	3
Other physical hurt	4
Don't know	5

4. Had this victim ever met their attacker(s) on any previous occasion? [Circle appropriate number.]

No	1
Yes	2
DK	3

5. Did the offence involve any loss of (or damage to) property or money (belonging either to an individual or to an organisation)? [Circle appropriate number.]

No	1	SKIP TO Q.7
Don't know	2	SKIP TO Q.7
Yes	3	ASK Q.6

6. Roughly what was the size of that loss? [Circle appropriate number.]

£10,000 or over	1
£500 or over	2
£100 or over	3
Under £100	4
Don't know	5

7. How many offenders were involved? [Circle appropriate number.]

One offender	1
Two offenders	2
Three or more offenders	3
Don't know	4

8. Was a suspect(s) ever identified? [Circle appropriate number.]

No	1	SKIP TO Q.10 [Paraphrase]
Yes	2	ASK Q.9

9. When was/were the suspect(s) identified? [Circle ALL appropriate numbers if different suspects identified at different stages.]

Before any HOLAB form/items were submitted to lab	1
After HOLAB form/items submitted and before FSS reported	2
After FSS reported	3

10. Was anyone ever arrested/charged (or warned of summons, or other process, eg caution)? [Circle appropriate number.]

No	1	SKIP TO Q.12
Yes	2	ASK Q.11

11. When was that person arrested (charged etc)? [Circle ALL appropriate numbers if different suspects arrested etc at different stages.]

Before any HOLAB form/items were submitted to lab	1
After HOLAB form/items submitted and before FSS reported	2
After FSS reported	3

12. To what extent were victim/witness(es) able to describe the offender to police—and in what kind of detail? [Witnesses include police witnesses.] [Circle FIRST APPROPRIATE number.]

Offender identified by name .... 1 ASK Q.13
Offender identified by own car no./unique identifier 2 ASK Q.13
Detailed description of the offender .... 3 ASK Q.13
Limited description of the offender .... 4 ASK Q.13
No description of offender .... 5 SKIP TO Q.14
Don't know .... 6 SKIP TO Q.14

13. From whom did you (or other officers) obtain statements—victim(s) or independent witness(es)? [Independent witnesses include police unless in victim capacity.] [Circle appropriate number.]

Statement from single victim only—not from indep. witness(es) 1
Statements from 2+ victims—not from indep. witness(es) 2
Statement(s) only from one or more independent witness(es) 3
Statements both from victim(s) and from indep. witness(es) 4
Other (specify ....) 5
Don't know 6

14. How much time elapsed between the offence and the initial arrival of the police at the scene of the crime (or, if more relevant, between the offence and personal contact between victim and police)? [Circle appropriate number.]

Under quarter hour 1
Under hour 2
Under 24 hours 3
Over 24 hours 4
Don't know 5

15. By whom was any forensic evidence found? [Circle ALL appropriate numbers.]

Detective(s) 1
Uniformed police 2
SOCO(s) 3
Forensic scientist(s) 4
Doctor(s) 5
Other (specify: ....) 6
Don't know 7

16. Were there any "contamination" problems relating to the scene of the crime, or to the victim? [Circle appropriate number.]

No .... 1 SKIP TO Q.18
Yes .... 2 ASK Q.17
Don't know ...... 3 ASK Q.17

17. What were these "contamination" problems? [Verbatim note to be taken.]

....

....

....

....

....

[Continue elsewhere if necessary]

The investigation: the role of forensic analysis

18. Looking back over the investigation, *up to the point at which you sent items to the Forensic Science Service*, which of the following events or actions occurred? [Circle ALL appropriate numbers.] [Show card to be used here.]

Suspect found at/near scene/gave self up	01
Suspect's ID known from an early stage	02
Victim's or other description acted upon	03
House to house enquiries	04
Suspect's ready access/obvious motive investigated	05
Search of property of possible suspects/accomplices	06
Observations/trap	07
Police knowledge/intelligence/use of informers	08
Fingerprint(s) found and searched against index	09
Photograph albums (mugshots) shown	10
Suspect implicated by accomplice	11
Suspect made written confession	12
Suspect made verbal admission/incriminating remarks	13
Other (specify ....)	14

19. Did you actively carry on with the investigation after the (first) HOLAB/ items had been submitted to the lab, but before the lab produced its report? ("Actively" = seeking new information, essentially.) [Circle appropriate number.]

No .... 1 SKIP TO Q.21
Yes .... 2 ASK Q.20

20. Explain what was done [only] *during that period*. [Brief note to be taken; use list/show card from Q.18 as a prompt, to fill brackets.]

....

....

....

.... [/] [/] [/] [/] [/]
[Continue elsewhere]

21. What made you decide to send items to the lab for analysis? [Verbatim note to be taken.]

....

....

....

[Continue elsewhere if necessary]

22. At the time when you sent items to the lab. what sort of hopes did you have [Circle appropriate number.]

Hoped crucial evidence would emerge 1

Hoped important evidence would emerge 2

Hoped useful evidence would emerge 3

Not very hopeful—acted "just in case..." 4

Not very hopeful—routine referral to FSS 5

23. Which of the following objectives did you have in mind in submitting items to the FSS? Select up to two from the list. [Use show card.] [Circle ONE or TWO appropriate numbers.]

To see if/how a crime was committed 1
For reference in future 2
To help identify a previously unidentified suspect(s) 3
To strengthen/validate the case against a suspect 4
Other (specify......................................) 5

24. INTERVIEWER CHECK—WERE TWO OBJECTIVES SELECTED? [Circle appropriate number.]

No .... 1 SKIP TO Q.26
Yes .... 2 ASK Q.25

25. Which was the main objective? [Circle appropriate number.]

To see if/how a crime was committed 1
For reference in future 2
To help identify a previously unidentified suspect(s) 3
To strengthen/validate the case against a suspect 4
Other 5

Police response to lab findings

26. In your view, did the FSS do what you had asked it to do (irrespective of delay or of the nature of its findings)? [Circle appropriate number.]

No 1   ASK Q.27
Don't know 2   ASK Q.27
Yes 3   SKIP TO Q.28

27. In what way did the FSS fail to do what was asked of it? [Verbatim note to be taken.]

....

....

....

....

[Continue elsewhere if necessary]

28. Was there any delay on the part of the lab—in producing its report— which inconvenienced the investigation or the prosecution? [Circle no.]

No 1   SKIP TO Q.30
DK 2   ASK Q.29
Yes 3   ASK Q.29

29. What was the effect of that delay? [Brief note to be taken.]

....

....

....

....

30. Did the report from the lab have any of the following three "positive" results? [Circle FIRST APPROPRIATE number.]

Strengthening or upholding of the case against a person already charged (or equivalent) 1   SKIP TO Q.32

Strengthening or upholding of the case against a previously uncharged person 2   ASK Q.31

A previously unsuspected (specific) person was shown to be implicated 3   ASK Q.31

None of these three "positive" developments occurred 4   SKIP TO Q.32

Don't know 5   SKIP TO Q.32

31. Was anybody subsequently charged as a result—either wholly or in part—of the lab report? [Circle appropriate answer.]

Yes, person charged wholly as a result of report 1

Yes, person charged largely as a result of report 2

Yes, person charged in part as result of report 3

Yes, person charged, but only marginally as a result of report 4

No, charges not brought, despite report 5

Don't know 6

32. Did the report from the lab have any of the following four "negative" results? [Circle the FIRST APPROPRIATE number.]

A person previously charged was fully cleared of suspicion 1   ASK Q.33

The case against a person previously charged was not strengthened or sustained 2   ASK Q.33

A person previously—merely—suspected was fully cleared of suspicion 3   ASK Q.33

The case against a person previously—merely—suspected was not strengthened or sustained 4   ASK Q.33

None of these four "negative" developments occurred 5   SKIP TO Q.35

Don't know 6   SKIP to Q.34

33. Which if any of the following courses of action did you then adopt? [Circle ALL appropriate numbers.]

To ask FSS to carry out more work (items already submitted) 1

To submit new material to FSS 2

To continue with the case/investigation on the basis of other evidence already available 3

To seek fresh ways of continuing with the case/investigation 4

To discontinue or put aside the case/investigation 5

34. Probe for further details. [Brief note to be taken.]

....

....

....

....

[Continue elsewhere if necessary]

35. Looking back to the time immediately after you'd got the report (and before the case had gone through the courts), how, at that point, would you have rated the contribution made by the scientific evidence? [Separate guidelines to be handed to investigating officer.] [Circle appropriate number.]

Scientific evidence made crucial contribution to the case 1
Scientific evidence made substantial contribution to the case 2
Scientific evidence made useful contribution to the case 3
Scientific evidence made minimal contribution to the case 4
Scientific evidence made little contribution to the case 5
Scientific evidence made no contribution to the case 6
Don't know/unclear at time 7

Final outcome of case: role of forensic evidence

36. Was case cleared up? [Circle appropriate number.]
No 1   ASK Q.37
Don't know/not yet—case still open 2   ASK Q.37
Yes 3   SKIP TO Q.39

37. Even though the case was not cleared up/is still open, was any benefit gained from consulting the FSS? [Brief note to be taken.]

....

....

....

....

[Continue elsewhere if necessary]

38. How likely is it that this offence will be cleared up at some future point? [Circle appropriate number.]

Clear-up very likely 1
Clear-up quite likely 2
Clear-up not particularly likely ... 3
Clear-up very unlikely 4
Don't know 5

39. What sort of clear-up was involved? [Circle appropriate number.]
Offender pleaded guilty .... 1 ASK Q.40
Offender convicted following trial .... 2 SKIP TO Q.41
Clear-up as TIC .... 3 SKIP TO Q.48
Other clear-up (specify ....) 4 SKIP TO Q.48

40. To what extent do you think that forensic evidence helped to produce this outcome? [Circle appropriate number.]

Guilty plea highly unlikely without forensic evidence 1
Guilty plea fairly unlikely without forensic evidence 2
Hard to be certain either way 3
Guilty plea fairly likely even without forensic evidence 4
Guilty plea highly likely even without forensic evidence 5

INTERVIEWER: IF Q.40 ANSWERED, SKIP TO Q.47

41. Did the—contested—trial occur in the Crown Court or in a magistrates' court? [Circle appropriate number.]

Crown Court 1

Magistrates' court 2

42. What sorts of evidence were used by the prosecution? [Circle ALL the appropriate numbers.]

Testimony of police witnesse(s) 1
Testimony of member(s) of public 2
Written confession 3
Verbal confession/incriminating remarks 4
FSS report and/or testimony of forensic scientist 5
Other (specify ....) 6

43. INTERVIEWER CHECK—WAS 5 (FORENSIC EVIDENCE) CIR-CLED IN Q.42? [Circle appropriate number.]

No .... 1 ASK Q.44

Yes .... 2 SKIP TO Q.45

44. Why was no forensic evidence presented? [Verbatim note to be taken.]

....

....

....

....

INTERVIEWER: IF Q.44 ANSWERED, SKIP TO Q.47

45. What form did the forensic evidence take? [Circle appropriate number.]

Written evidence only 1
Forensic scientist called to court but did not give evidence 2
Forensic scientist gave evidence 3
Don't know 4

46. How important, for the prosecution case, was any forensic evidence in helping to determine the outcome of the trial? [Circle appropriate number.]

Forensic evidence essential to prosecution case 1
Forensic evidence important to prosecution case 2
Forensic evidence a useful part of prosecution case 3
Forensic evid. of low value—but not harmful—to prosec'n 4
Forensic evidence made no clear impact either way 5
Forensic evidence was unhelpful to prosecution case 6
Don't know 7

47. What sentence was imposed (for the FSS-linked offence)? [Add together consecutive sentences.] [Circle appropriate number.]

Non-custodial sentence 1
Wholly suspended sentence of imprisonment 2
Imprisonment (immediate)—6 months or less (in total) 3
Imprisonment (immediate)—over 6 months, up to/including 12 months
.... 4
Imprisonment (immediate)—over 12 months, up to/including 2 years ...
.... 5
Imprisonment—over 2 years, up to/including 4 years 6
Imprisonment—over 4 years, up to/including 10 years 7
Imprisonment—over 10 years, up to/including life 8

48. How many previous convictions did the offender have for indictable offences (before the FSS-linked offence was committed)? [Circle the FIRST APPROPRIATE number.]

Offender 10 or more precons 1
Offender had 5 or more precons .. 2
Offender had between 1 and 5 precons
.... 3
Offender had no precons 4
Don't know 5

49. Was this offender habitually making financial gains from crime, when/if free? [Circle appropriate number.]

No 1   STOP
Don't know 2   STOP
Yes 3   ASK Q.50

50. If you were to make a guess, how much money do you think this offender could be expected to make from crime when/if free? [Circle FIRST APPROPRIATE number.]

> Offender could be expected to obtain £5,000 or more yearly, through crime, when/if free 1
> Offender could be expected to obtain £1,000 or more yearly, through crime, when/if free 2
> Offender could be expected to obtain an amount under £1,000 yearly, through crime, when/if free 3
> Don't know how much 4

OVERVIEW

A. Are there any aspects to this case *not* covered in the questionnaire which you think might be relevant?

....

....

....

....

B. In hindsight, is there any way in which you might have made different use of the FSS?

....

....

....

....

(GENERAL VIEWS ABOUT THE FSS: ASK AS APPROPRIATE)

C. In general, how useful do you find the Forensic Science Service, and why?

....

....

....

....

....

D. Do you see any scope for improving the FSS? How?

....

....

....

....

E. Do you see any scope for the police to make better or more effective use of the FSS? How?

....

....

....

....

....

F. Any other points?

....

....

....

....

....

....

....

....

....

....

....

....

....

....

....

....

References

Greenwood, T. W. and Petersilia, J. (1975). *The Criminal Investigation Process. Volume 1. Summary and Policy Implications.* Santa Monica: Rand Corporation.

Peterson, J. L., Bender, P. L. and Gilliland, M. V. K. (1982). *The Utilisation of the Forensic Sciences in Police Investigations: a review of the literature.* Unpublished paper, Center for Research in Law and Justice, University of Illinois, Chicago.

Peterson, J. L., Mihajlovic, S. and Gilliland, M. (1983). *Forensic Evidence and the Police: the effects of scientific evidence on criminal investigations. Final report.* Unpublished paper, Center for Research in Law and Justice, University of Illinois, Chicago.

Rosenthal, P. and Travnicek, D. A. (1974). *Analysis of Criminalistics Laboratory Effectiveness in Criminal Justice Systems.* Buffalo: Calspan Corporation.

Steer, D. (1980). *Uncovering Crime: the role of the police.* Royal Commission on Criminal Procedure. Research Study No. 7. London: HMSO.

Publications

* Out of print

6. *Hostels for probationers. A study of the aims, working and variations in effectiveness of male probation hostels with special reference to the influence of the environment on delinquency. Ian Sinclair. 1971. ix + 200pp. (11 340106 X).

7. *Prediction methods in criminology—including a prediction study of young men on probation. Frances H. Simon. 1971. xi + 234pp. (11 340107 8).

8. *Study of the juvenile liaison scheme in West Ham 1961–65. Marilyn Taylor. 1971. vi + 46pp. (11 340108 6).

9. *Exploration in after-care. I—After-care units in London, Liverpool and Manchester. Martin Silberman (Royal London Prisoners' Aid Society) and Brenda Chapman. II—After-care hostels receiving a Home Office grant. Ian Sinclair and David Snow (HORU). III—St. Martin of Tours House, Ayreh Leissner (National Bureau for Co-operation in Child Care). 1971. xi + 140pp. (11 340109 4).

10. A survey of adoption in Great Britain. Eleanor Grey in collaboration with Ronald M. Blunden. 1971. ix + 168pp. (11 340110 8).

11. *Thirteen-year-old approved school boys in 1962. Elizabeth Field, W. H. Hammond and J. Tizard. 1971. xi + 46pp. (11 34011 6).

12. Absconding from approved schools. R. V. G. Clarke and D. N. Martin. 1971. vi + 146pp. (11 340112 4).

13. An experiment in personality assessment of young men remanded in custody. H. Sylvia Anthony. 1972. viii + 79pp. (11 340113 2).

14. *Girl offenders aged 17–20 years. I—Statistics relating to girl offenders aged 17–20 years from 1960 to 1970. II—Re-offending by girls released from borstal or detention centre training. III—The problems of girls released from borstal training during their period on after-care. Jean Davies and Nancy Goodman. 1972. v + 77pp. (11 340114 0).

15. *The controlled trial in institutional research—paradigm or pitfall for penal evaluators? R. V. G. Clarke and D. B. Cornish. 1972. v + 33pp. (11 340115 9).

16. *A survey of fine enforcement. Paul Softley. 1973. v + 65pp. (11 340116 7).

17. *An index of social environment—designed for use in social work research. Martin Davies. 1973. vi + 63pp. (11 340117 5).

18. *Social enquiry reports and the probation service. Martin Davies and Andrea Knopt. 1973. v + 49pp. (11 340118 3).

19. *Depression, psychopathic personality and attempted suicide in a borstal sample. H. Sylvia Anthony. 1973. viii + 44pp. (0 11 340119 1).

20. *The use of bail and custody by London magistrates' courts before and after the Criminal Justice Act 1967. Frances Simon and Mollie Wetheritt. 1974. vi + 78pp. (0 11 340120 5).

21. Social work in the environment. A study of one aspect of probation practice. Martin Davies, with Margaret Rayfield. Alaster Calder and Tony Fowles. 1974. ix + 151pp. (0 11 340121 3).

22. Social work in prison. An experiment in the use of extended contact with offenders. Margaret Shaw, vii + 154pp. (0 11 340122 1).

23. Delinquency amongst opiate users. Joy Mott and Marilyn Taylor. vi + 31pp. (01 340663 0).

24. IMPACT. Intensive matched probation and after-care treatment. Vol. I—The design of the probation experiment and an interim evaluation. M. S. Folkard, A. J. Fowles, B. C. McWilliams, W. McWilliams, D. D. Smith, D. E. Smith and G. R. Walmsley. 1974. v + 54pp. (0 11 340664 9).

25. The approved school experience. An account of boys' experiences of training under differing regimes of approved schools, with an attempt to evaluate the effectiveness of that training. Anne B. Dunlop. 1974. vii + 124pp. (0 11 340665 7).

26. *Absconding from open prisons. Charlotte Banks, Patricia Mayhew and R. J. Sapsford. 1975. viii + 89pp. (0 11 340666 5).

27. Driving while disqualified. Sue Kriefman. 1975. vi + 136pp. (0 11 340667 3).

28. Some male offenders' problems. I—Homeless offenders in Liverpool. W. McWilliams. II—Casework with short-term prisoners. Julie Holborn. 1975. x + 147pp. (0 11 340668 1).

---

* Out of print

29. *Community service orders. K. Pease, P. Durkin, I. Earnshaw, D. Payne and J. Thorpe. 1975. viii + 80pp. (0 11 340669 X).

30. Field Wing Bail Hostel: the first nine months. Frances Simon and Sheena Wilson. 1975. viii + 55pp. (0 11 340670 3).

31. Homicide in England and Wales 1967–1971. Evelyn Gibson. 1975. iv + 59pp. (0 11 340753 X).

32. Residential treatment and its effects on delinquency. D. B. Cornish and R. V. G. Clarke. 1975. vi + 74pp. (0 11 340672 X).

33. Further studies of female offenders. Part A: Borstal girls eight years after release. Nancy Goodman, Elizabeth Maloney and Jean Davies. Part B: The sentencing of women at the London Higher Courts. Nancy Goodman, Paul Durkin and Janet Halton. Part C: Girls appearing before a juvenile court. Jean Davies. 1976. vi + 114pp. (0 11 340673 8).

34. *Crime as opportunity. P. Mayhew, R. V. G. Clarke, A. Sturman and J. M. Hough. 1976. vii + 36pp. (0 11 340674 6).

35. The effectiveness of sentencing: a review of the literature. S. R. Brody. 1976. v + 89pp. (0 11 340675 4).

36. IMPACT. Intensive matched probation and after-care treatment. Vol II—The results of the experiment. M. S. Folkard, D. E. Smith and D. D. Smith. 1976. xi + 400pp. (0 11 340676 2).

37. Police cautioning in England and Wales. J. A. Ditchfield. 1976. v + 31pp. (0 11 340677 2).

38. Parole in England and Wales. C. P. Nuttall, with E. E. Barnard, A. J. Fowles, A. Frost, W. H. Hammond, P. Mayhew, K. Pease, R. Tarling and M. J. Weatheritt. 1977. vi + 90pp. (0 11 340678 9).

39. Community service assessed in 1976. K. Pease, S. Billingham and I. Earnshaw. 1977. vi + 29pp. (0 11 340679 7).

40. Screen violence and film censorship: a review of research. Stephen Brody. 1977. vii + 179pp. (0 11 340680 0).

41. Absconding from borstals. Gloria K. Laycock. 1977. v + 82pp. (0 11 340681 9).

42. Gambling: a review of the literature and its implications for policy and research. D. B. Cornish. 1978. xii + 284pp. (0 11 340682 7).

43. Compensation orders in magistrates' courts. Paul Softley. 1978. v + 41pp. (0 11 340683 5).

44. Research in criminal justice. John Croft. 1978 iv + 16pp. (0 11 340684 3).

45. Prison welfare: an account of an experiment at Liverpool. A. J. Fowles. 1978. v + 34pp. (0 11 340685 1).

46. Fines in magistrates' courts. Paul Softley. 1978. v + 42pp. (0 11 340686 X).

47. Tackling vandalism. R. V. G. Clarke (editor), F. J. Gladstone, A. Sturman and Sheena Wilson (contributors). 1978. vi + 91pp. (0 11 340687 8).

48. Social inquiry reports: a survey. Jennifer Thorpe. 1979. vi + 55pp. (0 11 340688 6).

49. Crime in public view. P. Mayhew, R. V. G. Clarke, J. N. Burrows, J. M. Hough and S. W. C. Winchester. 1979. v + 36pp. (0 11 340689 4).

50. *Crime and the community. John Croft. 1979. v + 16pp. (0 11 340690 8).

51. Life-sentence prisoners. David Smith (editor), Christopher Brown, Joan Worth, Roger Sapsford and Charlotte Banks (contributors). 1979. iv + 51pp. (0 11 340691 6).

52. Hostels for offenders. Jane E. Andrews, with an appendix by Bill Sheppard. 1979. v + 30pp. (0 11 340692 4).

53. Previous convictions, sentence and reconviction: a statistical study of a sample of 5,000 offenders convicted in January 1971. G. J. O. Phillpotts and L. B. Lancucki. 1979. v + 55pp. (0 11 340693 2).

54. Sexual offences, consent and sentencing. Roy Walmsley and Karen White. 1979. vi + 77pp. (0 11 340694 0).

55. Crime prevention and the police. John Burrows, Paul Ekblom and Kevin Heal. 1979. v + 37pp. (0 11 340695 9).

---

* Out of print

56. Sentencing practice in magistrates' courts. Roger Tarling, with the assistance of Mollie Weatheritt. 1979. vii + 54pp. (0 11 340696).

57. Crime and comparative research. John Croft. 1979. iv + 16pp. (0 11 340697 5).

58. Race, crime and arrests. Philip Stevens and Carole F. Willis. 1979. v + 69pp. (0 11 340698 3).

59. Research and criminal policy. John Croft. 1980. iv + 14pp. (0 11 340699 1).

60. Junior attendance centres. Anne B. Dunlop. 1980. v + 47pp. (0 11 340770 9).

61. Police interrogation: an observational study in four police stations. Paul Softley, with the assistance of David Brown, Bob Forde, George Mair and David Moxon. 1980. vii + 67pp. (0 11 340701 7).

62. Co-ordinating crime prevention efforts. F. J. Gladstone. 1980. v + 74pp. (0 11 340702 5).

63. Crime prevention publicity: an assessment. D. Riley and P. Mayhew. 1980. v + 47pp. (0 11 340703 3).

64. Taking offenders out of circulation. Stephen Brody and Roger Tarling. 1980. v + 46pp. (0 11 340704 1).

65. *Alcoholism and social policy: are we on the right lines? Mary Tuck. 1980. v + 30pp. (0 11 340705 X).

66. Persistent petty offenders. Suzan Fairhead. 1981. vi + 78pp. (0 11 340706 8).

67. Crime control and the police. Pauline Morris and Kevin Heal. 1981. v + 71pp. (0 11 340707 6).

68. Ethnic minorities in Britain: a study of trends in their positions since 1961. Simon Field, George Mair, Tom Rees and Philip Stevens. 1981. v + 48pp. (0 11 340708 4).

69. Managing criminological research. John Croft. 1981. iv + 17pp. (0 11 340709 2).

70. Ethnic minorities, crime and policing: a survey of the experiences of West Indians and whites. Mary Tuck and Peter Southgate. 1981. iv + 50pp. (0 11 3240765 3).

71. Contested trials in magistrates' courts. Julie Vennard. 1982. v + 32pp. (0 11 340766 1).

72. Public disorder: a review of research and a study in one inner city area. Simon Field and Peter Southgate. 1982. v + 77pp. (0 11 340767 X).

73. Clearing up crime. John Burrows and Roger Tarling. 1982. vii + 31pp. (0 11 340768 8).

74. Residential burglary: the limits of prevention. Stuart Winchester and Hilary Jackson. 1982. v + 47pp. (0 11 340769 6).

75. Concerning crime. John Croft. 1982. iv + 16pp. (0 11 340770 X).

76. The British Crime Survey: first report. Mike Hough and Pat Mayhew. 1983. v + 62pp. (0 11 340789 6).

77. Contacts between police and public: findings from the British Crime Survey. Peter Southgate and Paul Ekblom. 1984. v + 42pp. (0 11 340771 8).

78. Fear of crime in England and Wales. Michael Maxfield. 1984. v + 51pp. (0 11 340772 6).

79. Crime and police effectiveness. Ronald V. Clarke and Mike Hough. 1984. iv + 33pp. (0 11 340773 4).

80. The attitudes of ethnic minorities. Simon Field. 1984. v + 50pp. (0 11 340774 2).

81. Victims of crime: the dimensions of risk. Michael Gottfredson. 1984. v + 54pp. (0 11 340775 0).

82. The tape recording of police interviews with suspects: an interim report. Carole Willis. 1984. v + 45pp. (0 11 340776 9).

83. Parental supervision and juvenile delinquency. David Riley and Margaret Shaw. 1985. v + 90pp. (0 11 340799 8).

84. Adult prisons and prisoners in England and Wales 1970–82: a review of the findings of social research. Joy Mott. 1985. vi + 73pp. (0 11 340801 3).

85. Taking account of crime: key findings from the 1984 British Crime Survey. Mike Hough and Pat Mayhew. 1985. vi + 115pp. (0 11 340810 2).

86. Implementing crime prevention measures. Tim Hope. 1985. vi + 82pp. (0 11 340812 9).

87. Resettling refugees: the lessons of research. Simon Field. 1985. vi + 62pp. (0 11 340815 3).

* Out of print

88. Investigating Burglary: the measurement of police performance. John Burrows. 1986. v + 36pp. (0 11 340824 2).

89. Personal violence. Roy Walmsley. 1986. vi + 87pp. (0 11 340827 7).

90. Police—public encounters. Peter Southgate with the assistance of Paul Ekblom. 1986. vi + 150pp. (0 11 340834 X).

91. Grievance procedures in prisons. John Ditchfield and Claire Austin. 1986. vi + 78pp. (0 11 340839 0).

ALSO

Designing out crime, R. V. G. Clarke and P. Mayhew (editors). 1980. vii + 186pp. (0 11 340732 7).

(This book collects, with an introduction, studies that were originally published in HORS 34, 47, 49, 55, 62 and 63 and which are illustrative of the 'situational' approach to crime prevention.)

Policing today. Kevin Heal, Roger Tarling and John Burrows (editors). 1985. v + 181pp. (0 11 340800 5).

(This book brings together twelve separate studies on police matters produced during the last few years by the Unit. The collection records some relatively little known contributions to the debate on policing.)

Managing criminal justice: a collection of papers. David Moxon (editor). 1985. vi + 222pp. (0 11 430811 0).

(This book brings together a number of studies bearing on the management of the criminal justice system. It includes papers by social scientists and operational researchers working within the Research and Planning Unit, and academic researchers who have studied particular aspects of the criminal process.)

Situational crime prevention: from theory into practice. Kevin Heal and Gloria Laycock (editors). 1986. vii + 166pp. (0 11 340826 9).

(Following the publication of Designing Out Crime, further research has been completed on the theoretical background to crime prevention. In drawing this work together this book sets down some of the theoretical concerns and discusses the emerging practical issues. It includes contributions by Unit staff as well as academics from this country and abroad.)

The above HMSO publications can be purchased from Government Bookshops or through booksellers.

The following Home Office research publications are available on request from the Home Office Research and Planning Unit, 50 Queen Anne's Gate, London, SW1H 9AT.

Research Unit Papers (RUP)

1. Uniformed police work and management technology. J. M. Hough. 1980.

2. Supplementary information on sexual offences and sentencing. Roy Walmsley and Karen White. 1980.

3. Board of Visitor adjudications. David Smith, Claire Austin and John Ditchfield. 1981.

4. Day centres and probations. Suzan Fairhead, with the assistance of J. Wilkinson-Grey. 1981.

Research and Planning Unit Papers (RPUP)

5. Ethnic minorities and complaints against the police. Philip Stevens and Carole Willis. 1982.

6. *Crime and public housing. Mike Hough and Pat Mayhew (editors). 1982.

7. *Abstracts of race relations research. George Mair and Philip Stevens (editors). 1982.

8. Police probationer training in race relations. Peter Southgate. 1982.

9. *The police response to calls from the public. Paul Ekblom and Kevin Heal. 1982.

* Out of print

10. City centre crime: a situational approach to prevention. Malcolm Ramsay. 1982.
11. Burglary in schools: the prospects for prevention. Tim Hope. 1982.
12. *Fine enforcement. Paul Softley and David Moxon. 1982.
13. Vietnamese refugees. Peter Jones. 1982.
14. Community resources for victims of crime. Karen Williams. 1983.
15. The use, effectiveness and impact of police stop and search powers. Carole Willis. 1983.
16. Acquittal rates. Sid Butler. 1983.
17. Criminal justice comparisons: the case of Scotland and England and Wales. Lorna J. F. Smith. 1983.
18. Time taken to deal with juveniles under criminal proceedings. Catherine Frankenburg and Roger Tarling. 1983.
19. Civilian review of complaints against the police: a survey of the United States literature. David C. Brown. 1983.
20. Police action on motoring offences. David Riley. 1983.
21. *Diverting drunks from the criminal justice system. Sue Kingsley and George Mair. 1983.
22. The staff resource implications of an independent prosecution system. Peter R. Jones. 1983.
23. Reducing the prison population: an explanatory study in Hampshire. David Smith, Bill Sheppard, George Mair and Karen Williams. 1984.
24. Criminal justice system model: magistrates' courts' sub-model. Susan Rice. 1984.
25. Measures of police effectiveness and efficiency. Ian Sinclair and Clive Miller. 1984.
26. Punishment practice by prison Boards of Visitors. Susan Iles, Adrienne Connors, Chris May, Joy Mott. 1984.
27. *Reparation, conciliation and mediation. Tony Marshall. 1984.
28. Magistrates domestic courts: new perspectives. Tony Marshall (editor). 1984.
29. Racism awareness training for the police. Peter Southgate. 1984.
30. Community constables: a study of policing initiative. David Brown and Susan Iles. 1985.
31. Recruiting volunteers. Hilary Jackson. 1985.
32. Juvenile sentencing: is there a tariff? David Moxon, Peter Jones and Roger Tarling. 1985.
33. Bringing people together: mediation and reparation projects in Great Britain. Tony Marshall and Martin Walpole. 1985.
34. Remands in the absence of the accused. Chris May. 1985.
35. Modelling the criminal justice system. Patricia M. Morgan. 1986.
36. The criminal justice system model: the flow model. Hugh Pullinger. 1986.
37. Burglary: police actions and victim views. John Burrows. 1986.
38. Unlocking community resources: four experimental government small grants schemes. Hilary Jackson. 1986.
39. The costs of discriminating: a review of the literature. Shirley Dex. 1986.

Research Bulletin

The Research Bulletin is published twice a year and consists mainly of short articles relating to projects which are part of the Home Office Research and Planning Unit's research programme.

---

* Out of print

Printed for Her Majesty's Stationery Office by Hobbs the Printers of Southampton
(3514/86) Dd239743 C13 2/87 G443